Australian Legendary Tales

Illustrated by Elizabeth Durack

Australian
Legendary
Tales

Collected by
K. LANGLOH PARKER

Selected and edited by
H. DRAKE-BROCKMAN

The Viking Press   New York

All rights reserved
Published in 1966 by The Viking Press, Inc.
625 Madison Avenue, New York, N.Y. 10022
Published simultaneously in Canada by
The Macmillan Company of Canada Limited
Library of Congress catalog card number: 66-14414

398.2   1. Folk Tales
2. Australia

Printed in the U.S.A.

Contents

About The Legends and Illustrations

THESE legends are important. They were collected many years ago by Mrs. Langloh Parker, who as Catherine Field grew up among the aborigines then living on her father's station. As a child she was saved from drowning by natives; as a married woman she continued to live among them at Bangate Station on the Narran River, New South Wales. To her they were first of all playmates and friends. Later-developed, more scholarly interests were never allowed to chill the warmth of human relationship. It is her own sympathetic yet completely objective attitude which helps to make these legends and tales so vivid, so dramatic, so alive with the breath of the people who first recounted them. Despite their adult wisdom, the legends possess a poetic quality, childlike in its simplicity, that should endear them not only to children but to the young in heart. Clear-cut character drawing and shrewd understanding of basic human behavior and motive make them both delightful and amusing. It would be difficult to find a better concise comment on social snobbery and maternal vanity than in "Dinewan the Emu and Goomble-gubbon the Turkey." The idea of family limitation for economic reasons, though savage in application, suggests how old in human reckoning much cherished "modern" thought may be! Nor is gentler insight lacking. The story of the little duck who, captured by a vicious water rat, hatched forth a platypus, is a parable of lonely motherhood as pathetic as it is brave. Serious readers will discover that these legends, taken as a whole, create an astonishingly vivacious picture of life in Australia, "as it was in the beginning."

Mrs. Langloh Parker believed her *Australian Legendary Tales,* published in London in 1896, to be the first considerable collection of aboriginal legends and tales. Andrew Lang, the celebrated writer, who was then also considered to be what today would be called a leading anthropologist, wrote an enthusiastic introduction. Reviewers and public throughout the world greeted the modest volume with delight.

Mrs. Parker was in fact one of the first people to write exclusively of the Australian aborigines as fellow creatures. Perhaps she was, indeed, the first to set forth, to any noteworthy extent, their own vision of themselves and their conditions of living, so far as she was able to reproduce their thoughts and speech forms in written English. However well-intentioned earlier serious writers may have been, there remains in their work a hint of patronage, of outside observance, of case-book approach.

It is Mrs. Parker's strength that she wrote simply, seriously, and spared no effort. If she does not penetrate the deeper mysteries of aboriginal custom and tradition, her background of everyday living—the belief in Baiame the All Father, the wanderings of Wurrunna the culture hero, the significance attached to Mullee Mullees, Doowis, Yowis, Mingga—is so ably suggested that a sense of real familiarity with native existence is created for the reader. Moreover, an apparently effortless ease lifts her stories into the realm of literature without sacrificing what in this case is vital—the essential quality of truth. None of the later legend writers have achieved the same happy union of matter and style.

Mrs. Parker makes her original intention clear in her preface to the first edition: "A neighbour of mine exclaimed, when I mentioned that I purposed making a small collection of the folk-lore legends of the tribe of blacks I knew so well living on this station, 'But have the blacks any legends?' thus showing that people live in a country, and yet know little of the aboriginal inhabitants. . . ."

No other country has stories quite like these. I, too, have lived among aborigines, and respected them as fellow humans. Nevertheless, when I read National Library copies of Mrs. Parker's legends, I was filled with regret that I had not known them all my life.

Perhaps, I thought, she had felt as a child as I felt—that she did not wish continually to read stories about European, American, Asiatic or even African flowers and fairies; about castles she had never seen, or strange minarets; about witches and princes and hobgoblins and genii. She, too, I thought, may have longed for satisfying tales about the soft bush creatures, the wicked snakes, the gay or spiteful birds. She, too, must have wanted to know if the people who lived here before we came, loving the land as we now love it, had made up fables like those handed down from the Greeks and Romans, or like the myths and sagas of the Norsemen who were among our own ancestors. Surely, I used to think, if a country is to be loved, it is necessary to have stories and poetry about its own soil and creatures. The older such stories are, the more they are founded on natural facts and behavior observed for centuries, the better, no matter how supernatural they may eventually become. It seemed to me that we had none, that we were doomed to wait till some were manufactured. Yet, all the time, here were these fascinating legends languishing out of print.

In this new edition a selection has been made from four books. Some of the stories are "woggi-gai," or fairy tales pure and simple. Many explain also the beginnings of things, and were believed in the same way that Europeans once believed the world was flat, and that the sun, moon and stars revolved overhead. But some were not told to the children, or even to their mothers. Many of the longer stories, especially those about Baiame the All Father, who lived in his sky camp, were religious, and so sacrosanct. Bora, or initiation, ceremonies were, and in some districts still are, as sacred to aborigines as church services to us.

But the legends show also how much the aborigines were, and in outlying districts still are, haunted by magic and superstition; and how much of their lives had to be spent in arduous food hunting; and how callous they were by our standards, though by theirs we were, and still frequently are, worse than callous in our disturbance of their traditional hunting grounds and hallowed places. The way of the future should be a way of mutual understanding and respect. For that reason I am happy to have the opportunity to help in handing on Mrs. Parker's admirable collection, once again, on behalf of the original authors.

Andrew Lang stated that a few drawings, used as illustrations in the original books, had been given to him by his brother Dr. Lang of Corowa. These were "from the sketch book of an untaught Australian native . . . using ink, a pointed stick, and paper . . . Probably no other member of his dying race ever illustrated a book." And probably even Andrew Lang could not dream of a Namatjira! Yet this nameless artist, indeed probably the first to have his work reproduced for the pleasure of the general reader, deserves mention here. The style of his drawings is imitative though lively—a talent now frequently displayed among aboriginal children—but far removed in spirit from the pre-white era masterpieces drawn on bark or baobab nuts. The fascinating drawings with which Elizabeth Durack now complements the text, often employing her knowledge of authentic aboriginal art forms, enhance both enjoyment and understanding, not only of the legends but also of the aboriginal creative mind.

In arranging this book I have been greatly helped by a number of people. Particularly I wish to thank Mrs. P. C. Cousins, niece to Mrs. Langloh Parker, for the loan of copies of her aunt's works; Professor A. P. Elkin for his kind assistance in scrutinizing the new glossary, and for helpful suggestions in the necessary simplification of difficult or doubtful spellings; Mr. Drake of the Perth Public Library for his unfailing interest in obtaining books or references; and Mrs. Marjorie Rees for her patience in the often confusing and tedious business of spelling unification and glossary making.

To conclude, the Euahlayi people of whom Mrs. Parker writes had a habit of singing charms over their babies to help them to be good, or to grow strong or clever, or to preserve them from danger. Perhaps one such, sadly abused in the past, can be recalled now at a moment of national growth. It was always sung to a child who was just beginning to make his own way in the world, and reaching out for everything:

> Kind be.
> Do not steal,
> Do not touch which to another belongs;
> Leave all such alone.
> Kind be.

H. Drake-Brockman

Because many of these illustrations are drawn in the aboriginal manner, the reader may be interested to meet an old man named Jubbul, who taught me to understand and appreciate the black man's pictorial art. Jubbul was a survivor of a north Australian tribe of the Ord River, but although geographically far removed from the makers of these legends he was of the same race, and thought and reasoned in the same way. He used to visit me in my grass studio on the banks of the big river, heralding his approach with discreet coughing and muttered injunctions to his retinue of scraggy dogs. He would examine my paintings very intently, sometimes slapping his thigh and exclaiming, "That's got him! That's *got* him!" Portraits were an unfailing source of wonder and delight to him, probably because a likeness, such as we know it, is never attempted by the aboriginal artist. Jubbul went about making a picture in quite a different manner, as he was pleased to demonstrate when assured of my real interest.

It should be remembered that a bark painting is not made to be hung "right way up" on a wall and looked at straight on. It is painted on the ground and looked at on the ground by a circle of observers; thus some sections are drawn vertically, some parallel and some in reverse. Nor is any bark painting complete without a verbal explanation by the artist, who fills in with words the parts of the story that are left out. Sometimes a few vertical strokes may represent a whole sequence of events that the artist has decided not to depict, perhaps because they do not fit, or are too complicated, vague or difficult to delineate. In this way a few random strokes may be very significant. On the other hand, a whole section may be filled with lines or circles that have no meaning at all, but are just put in, as Jubbul explained, for "look nice." "Look nice" seems, in fact, to play a most important part in the whole job.

Jubbul had a very clear conception of what he was going to put down and seldom changed a line. The whole was a kind of building up, and when complete there was always something supremely satisfying about the way the space was used. His designs were never trite or merely repetitive.

Jubbul taught me the difference between what he called "play-about" art and the serious religious art of the sacred caves and rock faces. To the novice the two would appear to become rather confused at times, but Jubbul always helped out by laughing uproariously at the appropriate moments.

I do not think the aboriginal method has been employed before in direct illustration by us. In the drawings of this style used here the compositions are my own conception, but individual figures are the aborigines' own and have been taken from carved nuts, bark paintings, caves, rock faces, boomerangs, shields, coolamons, emu eggs and pieces of mother-of-pearl. They are the work of many artists, some long dead and none known beyond the boundaries of their vanishing tribes. I am indebted to them all—but mostly to Jubbul; and although he died some years ago I like to think he survives a little in some of these illustrations.

ELIZABETH DURACK

Perth, Western Australia

Australian Legendary Tales

DINEWAN THE EMU AND GOOMBLE-GUBBON
THE TURKEY

Dinewan has hidden ten of her chicks under the big saltbush. This is after she fell for Goomble-gubbon's yarn and had chopped off her wings. (Can you find the tomahawk she did it with?) She is walking back to the Goomble-gubbon again now with only two of her chicks, to get her own back on the cunning bird.

Dinewan the Emu
and Goomble-gubbon the Turkey

DINEWAN the emu, being the largest bird, was acknowledged as king by the other birds. The Goomble-gubbons, the turkeys, were jealous of the Dinewans. Particularly was the Goomble-gubbon mother jealous of the Dinewan mother. She would watch with envy the high flight of the Dinewans, and their swift running. And she always fancied that the Dinewan mother flaunted her superiority in her face, for whenever Dinewan alighted near Goomble-gubbon after a long, high flight, she would flap her big wings and begin booing in her pride, not the loud booing of the male bird but a little, triumphant, satisfied booing noise of her own, which never failed to irritate Goomble-gubbon when she heard it.

Goomble-gubbon used to wonder how she could put an end to Dinewan's supremacy. She decided that she would be able to do so only by injuring her wings and checking her power of flight. But the question that troubled her was how to gain this end. She knew she would gain nothing by having a quarrel with Dinewan and fighting her, for no Goomble-gubbon would stand any chance

15

against a Dinewan. There was evidently nothing to be gained by an open fight. She would have to gain her end by cunning.

One day, when Goomble-gubbon saw Dinewan in the distance coming toward her, she squatted down and drew in her wings in such a way as to look as if she had none.

After Dinewan had been talking to her for some time, Goomble-gubbon said, "Why do you not imitate me and do without wings? Every bird flies. The Dinewans, to be the king of birds, should do without wings. When all the birds see that I can do without wings, they will think I am the cleverest bird and they will make a Goomble-gubbon king."

"But you have wings," said Dinewan.

"No, I have no wings."

And indeed she looked as if her words were true, so well were her wings hidden as she squatted in the grass.

Dinewan went away after a while and thought much of what she had heard. She talked it all over with her mate, who was as disturbed as she was. They made up their minds that it would never do to let the Goomble-gubbons reign in their stead, even if they had to lose their wings to save their kingship.

At length they decided to sacrifice their wings. The Dinewan mother showed the example by persuading her mate to cut off hers with a kumbu, or stone tomahawk, and then she did the same to his.

As soon as the operations were over the Dinewan mother lost no time in letting Goomble-gubbon know what they had done. She ran swiftly down to the plain where she had left Goomble-gubbon, and finding her still squatting there, she said, "See, I have followed your example. I have now no wings. They are cut off."

"Ha! ha! ha!" laughed Goomble-gubbon, jumping up

and dancing around with joy at the success of her plot. As she danced around she spread out her wings, flapped them and said, "I have taken you in, old stumpy wings. I have my wings yet. You are fine birds, you Dinewans, to be chosen kings, when you are so easily taken in. Ha! ha! ha!"

And, laughing derisively, Goomble-gubbon flapped her wings right in front of Dinewan, who rushed toward her to punish her treachery. But Goomble-gubbon flew away, and, alas, the now wingless Dinewan could not follow her.

Brooding over her wrongs, Dinewan walked away, vowing she would be revenged. But how? That was the question that she and her mate failed to answer for some time.

At length the Dinewan mother thought of a plan and prepared at once to execute it.

She hid all her young Dinewans but two under a big saltbush. Then she walked off to Goomble-gubbon's plain with the two young ones following her. As she walked off the morilla, or pebbly ridge, where her home was, onto the plain, she saw Goomble-gubbon out feeding with her twelve young ones.

After exchanging a few remarks in a friendly manner with Goomble-gubbon, she said to her, "Why do you not imitate me and have only two children? Twelve are too many to feed. If you keep so many they will never grow to be big birds like the Dinewans. The food that would make big birds of two would only starve twelve."

Goomble-gubbon said nothing, but she thought it might be so. It was impossible to deny that the young Dinewans were much bigger than the young Goomble-gubbons, and she discontentedly walked away, wondering whether her young ones were smaller than the Dinewans because there were so many more of them. It would be grand, she thought, to grow as big as the Dinewans. But she remembered the trick she had played on Dinewan, and she thought that perhaps she was being fooled in her turn. She looked back to where the Dinewans fed, and as she saw how much bigger the two young ones were than any of hers, once more mad envy of Dinewan possessed her.

She determined not to be outdone. Rather, she would kill all her young ones but two.

She said, "The Dinewans shall not be the king birds of the plains. The Goomble-gubbons shall replace them. They shall grow as big as the Dinewans, and shall keep their wings and fly, which now the Dinewans cannot do."

And straightway Goomble-gubbon killed all her young ones but two.

Then back she came to where the Dinewans were still feeding.

When Dinewan saw her coming and noticed she had only two young ones with her, she called out, "Where are all your young ones?"

Goomble-gubbon answered, "I have killed them, and have only two left. Those will have plenty to eat now, and will soon grow as big as your young ones."

"You cruel mother to kill your children. You greedy mother. Why, I have twelve children and I find food for them all. I would not kill one for anything, not even if by so doing I could get back my wings. There is plenty for all. Look at how the saltbush covers itself with berries to feed my big family. See how the grasshoppers come hopping around, so that we can catch them and fatten on them."

"But you have only two children."

"I have twelve. I will go and bring them to show you."

Dinewan ran off to her saltbush where she had hidden her ten young ones.

Soon she was to be seen coming back—running with her neck stretched forward, her head thrown back with pride and the feathers of her booboo-tella, or tail, swinging as she ran, booing out the while her queer throat-noise, the Dinewan song of joy. The pretty, soft-looking little ones with their striped skins ran beside her, whistling their baby Dinewan note.

When Dinewan reached the place where Goomble-gubbon was, she stopped her booing and said in a solemn tone, "Now you see my words are true. I have twelve young ones, as I said. You can gaze at my loved ones and think of your poor murdered children. And while you do so I will tell you the fate of your descendants forever. By trickery and deceit you lost the Dinewans their wings, and now forevermore, as long as a Dinewan has no wings, so shall a Goomble-gubbon lay only two eggs and have only two young ones. We are quits now. You have your wings and I my children."

And ever since then a Dinewan, or emu, has had no wings, and a Goomble-gubbon, or turkey of the plains, has laid only two eggs in a season.

HOW THE SUN WAS MADE

Here is the good spirit who decided to keep the fire going to light the world each day. Around him is the emu, the native companion, or crane, and the Goo-goor-gaga. Up beside the spirit's head is the egg just after the native companion had thrown it. The part about the yolk igniting the firewood in the sky is left out. The dots in the "look-nice" part represent all the talk that went on at the beginning of the story and later the chuckling of the Goo-goor-gaga.

How the Sun Was Made

For a long time there was no sun, only a moon and stars. That was before there were men on the earth, only birds and beasts, all of which were many sizes larger than they are now.

One day Dinewan the emu and Brolga the native companion, or crane, were on a large plain near the Murrumbidgee. There they were, quarreling and fighting. Brolga, in her rage, rushed to the nest of Dinewan and seized from it one of the huge eggs, which she threw with all her force up to the sky. There it broke on a heap of firewood, which burst into flame as the yellow yolk spilled all over it. The flame lit up the world below, to the astonishment of every creature on it. They had been used to only the semidarkness, and were dazzled by such brightness.

A good spirit who lived in the sky saw how bright and beautiful the earth looked when lit up by this blaze. He thought it would be a good thing to make a fire every day, which from that time he has done. All night he and his attendant spirits collect wood and heap it up. When the heap is nearly big enough, they send out the morning star to warn those on earth that the fire will soon be lit.

The spirits, however, found this warning was not sufficient, for those who slept saw it not. Then the spirits thought they must have some noise made at dawn of day, to herald the coming of the sun and waken the sleepers. But for a long time they could not decide to whom should be given this office.

At last one evening they heard the laughter of Goo-goor-gaga the laughing jackass ringing through the air.

"That is the noise we want," they said.

Then they told Goo-goor-gaga that, as the morning star faded and the day dawned, he was every morning to laugh his loudest, that his laughter might awaken all sleepers before sunrise. If he would not agree to do this, then no more would they light the sun fire, but let the earth be ever in twilight again.

But Goo-goor-gaga saved the light for the world.

He agreed to laugh his loudest at every dawn of day, which he has done ever since, making the air ring with his loud cackling, "Goo goor gaga, goo goor gaga, goo goor gaga."

When the spirits first light the fire, it does not throw out much heat. But by the middle of the day, when the whole heap of firewood is in a blaze, the heat is fierce. After that it begins to die gradually away until only red embers are left at sunset; and they quickly die out, except a few the spirits cover up with clouds, and save to light the heap of wood they get ready for the next day.

Children are not allowed to imitate the laughter of Goo-goor-gaga, lest he should hear them and cease his morning cry.

If children do laugh as he does, an extra tooth grows above their eyetooth, so that they carry a mark of their mockery in punishment for it. Well the good spirits know that if ever a time comes wherein the Goo-goor-gagas cease laughing to herald the sun, then the time will have come when no more Daens, or blackfellows, are seen in the land, and darkness will reign once more.

The Southern Cross

In the very beginning when Baiame, the sky king, walked the earth, out of the red ground of the ridges he made two men and a woman. When he saw that they were alive he showed them such plants as they should eat to keep life; then he went on his way.

For some time they lived on the plants he had shown them. Then came a drought, and plants grew scarce, and when one day a man killed a kangaroo rat, he and the woman ate some of its flesh; but the other man would not eat though he was famished for food, and lay as one dead.

Again and again the woman told him it was good and pressed him to eat.

Annoyed, weak as he was he rose and walked angrily away toward the sunset, while the other two still ate hungrily.

When they had finished they looked for him, found he had gone some distance and went after him. Over the sandhills, over the pebbly ridges they went, losing sight of him from time to time. When they reached the edge of the coolabah plain they saw their comrade on the other side, by the river. They called to him to stop, but he heeded them not. On he went until he reached a huge yaraän, or white gum tree, beneath which he fell to the ground. As he lay there dead they saw beside him a black figure with two huge fiery eyes. This figure raised him into the tree and dropped him into its hollow center.

While still speeding across the plain, they heard so terrific a burst of thunder that they fell startled to the ground. When they raised themselves they gazed wonderingly toward the giant gum tree. They saw it being lifted from the earth and passing through the air toward the southern sky. They could not see their lost comrade, but fiery eyes gleamed from the tree. Suddenly, a raucous shrieking broke the stillness. They saw it came from two yellow-crested white cockatoos flying after the vanishing tree. Mooyi, they called them.

On went the Spirit Tree. After it flew the Mooyi, shrieking loudly to it to stop, so that they might reach their roosting place in it.

At last the tree planted itself near the Warrambool, or Milky Way, which leads to where the sky gods live. When it seemed quite still, the tree gradually disappeared from their sight. They saw only four fiery eyes shine out. Two were the eyes of Yowi, the spirit of death. The other two were the eyes of the first man to die.

The Mooyi fly after the tree, trying always to reach their roost again.

When all nature realized that the passing of this man meant that death had come into the world, there was wailing everywhere. The swamp oak trees sighed incessantly, the gum trees shed tears of blood, which crystallized into red gum.

To this day to the tribes of that part, the Southern Cross is known as Yaraändoo, the place of the white gum tree. And the north and south points of the cross are called Mooyi, the white cockatoos.

So is the first coming of death remembered by the tribes, to whom the Southern Cross is a reminder.

THE BEGINNING OF THE NARRAN LAKE

*Nearly all the story is here if you look hard enough. Baiame's two
wives are in one corner with their carrying baskets; there are the
frogs and yams they caught and here are the two crocodiles just
before they swallowed the poor women. All the center part is
Baiame's worried state of mind and his tracks following along for
miles and miles. Baiame killing the crocodiles is left out, but there
are his wives lying on the ground with ants crawling over them
and stinging them back to life. The last part is about the lake and
all the birds and fish Baiame arranged to live in it forever after.*

The Beginning of the Narran Lake

OLD Baiame said to his two young wives, Birra-nulu and Kunnan-beili, "I have stuck a white feather between the hind legs of a bee, and am going to let it go and then follow it to its nest, that I may get honey. While I go for the honey, go you two out and get frogs and yams, then meet me at Coorigil Spring, where we will camp, for sweet and clear is the water there."

The wives, taking their goolays, or net bags, and yam sticks, went out as he told them. Having gone far, and dug out many yams and frogs, they were tired when they reached Coorigil, and seeing the cool, fresh water they longed to bathe. But first they built a bough shade, and there left the goolays holding their food, and the yams and frogs they had found.

When their camp was ready for the coming of Baiame, who having wooed his wives with a nulla-nulla, or club, kept them obedient by fear of the same weapon, then went the girls to the spring to bathe. Gladly they plunged in, having first divested themselves of their goomillas, or string belts, which they were still young enough to wear, and which they left on the ground near the spring.

Scarcely were they enjoying the cool rest the water gave their hot, tired limbs, when they were seized and swallowed by two Kurrias, or crocodiles.

Having swallowed the girls, the Kurrias dived into an opening in the side of the spring, which was the entrance to an underground watercourse leading to the Narran River. Through this passage they went, taking all the water from the spring with them into the Narran, whose course they also dried as they went along.

Meantime, Baiame, unwitting of the fate of his wives, was honey hunting. He had followed the bee with the white feather on it for some distance. Then the bee flew onto some boodha, or saltbush flowers, and would move no farther.

Baiame said, "Something has happened, or the bee would not stay here and refuse to move on toward its nest. I must go to Coorigil Spring and see if my wives are safe. Something terrible has surely happened."

And Baiame turned in haste toward the spring.

When he reached there he saw the bough shed his wives had made, he saw the yams they had dug from the ground, and he saw the frogs; but Birra-nulu and Kun-nan-beili he saw not.

He called aloud for them. But no answer. He went toward the spring; on the edge of it he saw the goomillas of his wives. He looked into the spring and, seeing it dry, he said, "It is the work of the Kurrias. They have opened the underground passage and gone with my wives to the river, and opening the passage has dried the spring. Well do I know where the passage joins the Narran, and there will I swiftly go."

Arming himself with spears and woggars, or wooden axes, he started in pursuit.

He soon reached the deep hole where the underground

channel of the Coorigil joined the Narran. There he saw what he had never seen before, namely, this deep hole gone dry. And he said, "They have emptied the holes as they went along, taking the water with them. But well know I the deep holes of the river. I will not follow the bend, thus trebling the distance I have to go, but I will cut across from big hole to big hole, and by so doing I may yet get ahead of the Kurrias."

Swiftly on sped Baiame, making short cuts from big hole to big hole, and his tracks are still marked by the morillas, or pebbly ridges, that stretch down the Narran, pointing in toward the deep holes.

Every hole as he came to it he found dry, until at last he reached the end of the Narran. The hole there was still quite wet and muddy. Then he knew he was near his enemies, and soon he saw them.

He managed to get, unseen, a little way ahead of the Kurrias. He hid himself behind a big dheal tree. As the Kurrias came near they separated, one turning to go in another direction. Quickly Baiame hurled one spear after another, wounding both Kurrias, who writhed with pain and lashed their tails furiously, making great hollows in the ground, which the water they had brought with them quickly filled. Thinking they might again escape him, Baiame drove them from the water with his spears, and then, at close quarters, he killed them with his woggaras.

And ever afterward, at floodtime, the Narran flowed into this hollow which the Kurrias in their writhings had made.

When Baiame saw that the Kurrias were quite dead, he cut them open and took out the bodies of his wives. They were covered with wet slime and seemed quite lifeless, but he carried them and laid them on two nests of red ants. Then he sat down at some little distance and watched them. The ants quickly covered the bodies, cleaned them rapidly of the wet slime, and soon Baiame noticed the muscles of the girls twitching.

"Ah," he said, "there is life, they feel the sting of the ants."

Almost as he spoke came a sound as of a thunderclap, but the sound seemed to come from the ears of the girls. And as the echo was dying away, slowly the girls rose to their feet. For a moment they stood apart, a dazed expression on their faces. Then they clung together, shaking as if stricken with a deadly fear. But Baiame came to them and explained how they had been rescued from the Kurrias by him. He bade them to beware of ever bathing in the deep holes of the Narran, lest such holes be the haunt of Kurrias.

Then he bade them look at the water now at Boogira, and said, "Soon will the black swans find their way here, the pelicans and the ducks; where there was dry land and stones in the past, in the future there will be water and waterfowl. From henceforth, when the Narran runs it will run into this hole, and by the spreading of its waters will a big lake be made."

And what Baiame said has come to pass, as the Narran Lake shows, with its large sheet of water, spreading for miles, the home of thousands of wildfowl.

The Bora of Baiame

W O R D had been passed from tribe to tribe telling, now that the season was good, that there must be a great gathering of the tribes. And the place fixed for the gathering was Googoorewon, the place of trees.

The old men whispered that it should be the occasion for a Bora, but this the women must not know. Old Baiame, who was a great wirinun, said he would take his two sons, Ghinda-inda-mui and Booma-ooma-nowi, to the gathering of the tribes, for the time had come when they should be made young men, that they might be free to marry wives, eat emu flesh and learn to be warriors.

As tribe after tribe arrived at Googoorewon, each took up a position at one of the various points of the ridges, surrounding the clear open space where the corroborees were to be. The Wahn, crows, had one place; the Du-mer, pigeons, another; the Madhi, dogs, another and so on; Baiame and his tribe, Baiamul the black swan tribe, Ooboon the blue-tongued lizard and many other tribes. Each had their camp at a different spot.

When all had arrived, there were hundreds and hun-

THE BORA OF BAIAME

The great concourse of tribes meets for the sacred man-making ceremony. The circle in the center is the part cleared for the dancers. As much of the story as could possibly fit is drawn, though the part about the women and their dayoorls is left out; but there you can see the angry widow working her magic.

dreds assembled, and many and varied were the nightly
corroborees, each tribe trying to beat the other in the
fancifulness of their painted getup and the novelty of their
newest songs and dances. By day there was much hunting
and feasting, by night much dancing and singing; pledges
of friendship were exchanged, a dillibag for a boomerang,
and so on. Young daughters were given to old warriors,
old women given to young men, unborn girls promised to
old men, babies in arms promised to grown men. Many
and diverse were the agreements entered into, and always
were the wirinuns, or clever men, consulted.

After some days the wirinuns told the men of the tribes
that they were going to hold a Bora. But on no account
must the women know. Day by day they must all go forth
as if to hunt, and then prepare, in secret, the Bora ground.

Out went the men each day. They cleared a very large
circle quite clean. Then they built an earthen dam around
this circle and cleared a pathway leading into the thick
bush from the circle, and built a dam on either side of this
pathway.

When all these preparations were finished they had,
as usual, a corroboree at night.

After this had been going on for some time, one of the
old wirinuns walked right away from the crowd as if he
were sulky. He went to his camp, to where he was followed by another wirinun, and presently the two old fellows began fighting. Suddenly, when the attention of the
blacks was fixed on this fight, there came a strange, whizzing, whirring noise from the scrub around. The women
and children shrank together, for the sudden, uncanny
noise frightened them. And they knew that it was made by
the spirits who were coming to assist at the initiation of
the boys into young manhood.

(The noise really sounded, if you had not the dread of

spirits in your mind, just as if someone had a circular piece of wood at the end of a string and were whirling it round and round.)

As the noise went on, the women said, in awestruck tones, "Gurraymi," (that is, "Bora devil,") and clutched their children tighter to them.

The boys said, "Gayandi," and their eyes extended with fear. "Gayandi" meant Bora devil too, but the women must not even use the same word as the boys and men to express the Bora spirit, for all concerning the mysteries of Bora are sacred from the ears, eyes or tongues of women.

The next day a shift of the camps was made. The young people and women were moved inside the big ring that the blackfellows had made. This move was attended with a certain amount of ceremony.

In the afternoon, before the move had taken place, all the blackfellows left their camps and went away into the scrub. Then, just about sundown, they were all to be seen walking in single file out of the scrub, along the path which they had previously banked on each side. Every man held a fire stick in one hand and a green switch in the other. When these men reached the middle of the enclosed ring, it was time for the young people and women to leave the old camps and move into the Bora ring. Inside this ring they made new camps, had their suppers and corroboreed, as on previous evenings, up to a certain stage.

On this occasion, before that stage arrived, Baiame, who was the greatest of the wirinuns present, had shown his power in a remarkable way.

For some days the Madhi had been behaving with a great want of respect for the wise men of the tribes. Instead of treating their sayings and doings with the silent awe wirinuns always expect, they had kept up an incessant chatter and laughter among themselves, playing and shouting as if the tribes were not about to perform their most sacred rites. Frequently the wirinuns sternly bade them be silent. But warnings were useless; gaily chattered and laughed the Madhi.

At length Baiame, mightiest and most famous of the wirinuns, rose, strode over to the camp of the Madhi and said fiercely to them, "I, Baiame, whom all the tribes hold in honor, have thrice bade you Madhi cease your chatter and laughter. But you heeded me not. To my voice were added the voices of the wirinuns of other tribes. But you heeded not. Think you the wirinuns will make any of your tribe young men when you heed not the words of the wise men? No, I tell you. From this day forth no Madhi shall speak again as men speak. You wish to make noise, to be a noisy tribe and a disturber of men; a tribe who cannot keep quiet when strangers are in the camp; a tribe who understand not sacred things. So be it! You and your descendants shall forever make a noise. But it shall not be the noise of speech, or the noise of laughter. It shall be the noise of barking and the noise of howling. And from this day if ever a Madhi speaks, woe to those who hear him, for even as they hear they shall be turned to stone."

And as the Madhi opened their mouths, and tried to laugh and speak mocking words, they found, even as Baiame said, that they could not. They could but bark and howl; the powers of speech and laughter they had lost.

And as they realized their loss, into their eyes came a look of yearning and dumb entreaty, which will be seen in the eyes of their descendants forever. A feeling of wonder and awe fell on the various camps as they watched Baiame march back to his tribe.

When Baiame was seated again in his camp, he asked the women why they were not grinding doonbur, or grass seed. And the women said, "Gone are our dayoorls, and we know not where."

"You lie," said Baiame. "You have lent them to the Du-mer, who came so often to borrow, though I bade you not lend."

"No, Baiame, we lent them not."

"Go to the camp of the Du-mer, and ask for your dayoorls."

The women, in fear of the same fate as the Madhi if they disobeyed, went; though well they knew they had not lent the dayoorls, or grinding stones.

As they went they asked at each camp if the tribe there would lend them a dayoorl, but at each camp they were given the same answer, namely, that the dayoorls were gone and none knew where. The Du-mer had asked to borrow them, and each time been refused, yet had the grinding stones gone.

As the women went on they heard a strange noise, as of the cry of spirits, a sound like a smothered "oom, oom."

The cry sounded high in the air through the tops of trees, then low on the ground through the grasses, until it seemed as if the spirits were everywhere.

The women clutched tighter their fire sticks, and said, "Let us go back. The Wunda are about.'

And swiftly they sped toward their camp, hearing ever in the air the "oom, oom, oom" of the spirits.

They told Baiame that all the tribes had lost their dayoorls, and that the spirits were about, and even as they spoke came the sound of "oom, oom, oom, oom," at the back of their own camp.

The women crouched together, but Baiame flashed a fire stick whence came the sound, and as the light flashed on the place he saw no one, but, stranger than all, he saw two dayoorls moving along, and yet could see no one moving them, and as the dayoorls moved swiftly away, louder and louder rose the sound of "oom, oom, oom, oom," until the air seemed full of invisible spirits.

Then Baiame knew that indeed the Wunda, or spirits, were about, and he too clutched his fire stick and went back into his camp.

In the morning it was seen that not only were all the dayoorls gone, but the camp of the Du-mer was empty and they too had gone.

When no one would lend the Du-mer dayoorls, they had said, "Then we can grind no doonbur unless the Wunda bring us stones."

And scarcely were the words said before they saw a dayoorl moving toward them.

At first they thought it was their own skill which enabled them only to express a wish to have it realized. But as dayoorl after dayoorl glided into their camp, and passing through, moved on, and when, as they moved, the sound of "oom, oom, oom, oom," could be heard everywhere, then the Du-mer knew it was the Wunda at work. And it was borne in upon them that where the dayoorls went they must go, or they would anger the spirits who had moved them through their camp.

So the Du-mer gathered up their belongings and followed in the track of the dayoorls, which had cut a pathway from Googoorewon to Girraween, the place of flowers, down which, in high floods, is now a watercourse.

From Girraween, on the dayoorls went to Dirangibirra, and after them the Du-mer. Dirangibirra is between Brewarrina and Widder Murtee, and there the dayoorls piled themselves up into a mountain, and there for the future had the blacks to go when they wanted good grinding stones. And the Du-mer were changed into pigeons, with a cry like the spirits of "oom, oom, oom."

Another strange thing happened at this big Bora.

A tribe called Ooboon were camped at some distance from the other tribes. When any stranger went to their camp, it was noticed that the big man of the Ooboon would come out and flash a light on him, which killed him instantly. And no one knew what this light was, that carried death in its gleam.

At last Wahn the crow said, "I will take my biggest boreen and go and see what this means. You others, do not follow me too closely, for though I have planned how to save myself from the deadly gleam, I might not be able to save you."

Wahn walked into the camp of the Ooboon, and as their chief turned to flash the light on him he put up his boreen, or wooden shield, and completely shading himself from it, called aloud in a deep voice, "Wah, wah, wah, wah," which so startled Ooboon that he dropped his light and said, "What is the matter? You startled me. I did not know who you were and might have hurt you, though I had no wish to, for the Wahn are my friends."

"I cannot stop now," said Wahn. "I must go back to my camp. I have forgotten something I wanted to show you. I'll be back soon."

And so saying, swiftly ran Wahn back to where he had left his boondi, or club, then back he came almost before Ooboon realized that he had gone. Back he came, and stealing up behind Ooboon dealt him a blow with his boondi that avenged amply the victims of the deadly light, by stretching the big man of the Ooboon a corpse on the ground at his feet.

Then crying triumphantly, "Wah, wah, wah," back to his camp went Wahn and told what he had done.

This night, when the Bora corroboree began, all the women relations of the boys who were to be made young men corroboreed all night. Toward the end of the night all the young women were ordered into bough humpies, or shelters, which had been made previously all around the edge of the embankment surrounding the ring. The old women stayed on.

The men who were to have charge of the boys to be made young men were now told to be ready each to seize hold of his special charge, in order to carry him off down the beaten track to the scrub.

When every man had, at a signal, taken his charge on his shoulder, they all started dancing around the ring.

Then the old women were told to come and say good-by to the boys; afterward they were ordered to join the young women in the humpies.

About five men watched them pass into the humpies, then pulled the boughs down on top of them so that they might see nothing further.

When the women were safely imprisoned beneath the boughs, the men carrying the boys swiftly disappeared down the track into the scrub.

When they were out of sight, the five blackfellows went and pulled the boughs away and released the women, who went to their camps. But however curious the women were as to what rites attended the boys' initiation into manhood, they knew no questions would gain any information. In some months' time they might see their boys return minus a front tooth, perhaps, and with some extra scarifications or weals on their bodies, but beyond that, and a knowledge of the fact that the boys had not been allowed to look on the face of a woman since their disappearance into the scrub, the women were never told anything.

The next day the tribes made ready to travel to the place of the little Bora, which would be held in about four days, at about ten miles from the scene of the big Bora.

At the place of the little Bora a ring of grass is made instead of one of earth. The tribes all travel together there, camp and have a corroboree. The young women are sent to bed early, and the old women stay until the time when the boys say farewell to them; the boys are brought in and allowed to say a last good-by to the old women. Then they are taken away by the men who have charge of them, all together.

They stay together for a short time, then separate, each man with his one boy going in a different direction. The man keeps strict charge of the boy for at least six months, during which time he may not even look at his own mother. At the end of this period he may come back to his tribe, but the effect of his isolation is that he is too wild and frightened to speak even to his mother, from whom at first he runs away if she approaches him. By degrees the strangeness wears off.

But at this Bora of Baiame, the tribes were not destined to meet the boys at the little Bora.

Just as they were gathering up their goods for a start, into the camp staggered Millin-dulu-nubba the widow, crying, "You all left me, widow that I am, with my large family of children, to travel alone. How could the little feet of my children keep up with you? Can my back bear more than one goolay? Have I more than two arms and one back? Then how could I come swiftly with so many children? Yet none of you stayed to help me. And as you went from each water hole you drank all the water. When, tired and thirsty, I reached a water hole and my children cried for a drink, what did I find to give them? Mud, only mud. Then, thirsty and worn, my children crying and their mother helpless to comfort them, on we came to the next hole. What did we see, as we strained our eyes to find water? Mud, only mud. As we reached hole after hole and found only mud, one by one my children lay down and died; died for want of a drink, which Millin-dulu-nubba, their mother, could not give them.

As she spoke, swiftly went a woman to her with a wirree of water.

"Too late, too late," she said. "Why should a mother live when her children are dead?"

And she lay back with a groan.

But as she felt the water cool her parched lips and soften her swollen tongue she made a final effort, rose to her feet and, waving her hands around the camps of the tribes, cried aloud, "You were in such haste to get here. You shall stay here. Goo gool gai ya. Goo gool gai ya. Turn into trees. Turn into trees.

Then back she fell, dead.

And as she fell, the tribes that were standing around the edge of the ring before gathering their goods and preparing to go, and toward whom her hand pointed as it waved around, all turned into trees.

There they now stand. And the tribes in the background were also changed, each according to the name they were known by, into birds or beasts of the same name. The barking Mahdi into dogs, the Baiamul into black swans, the Wahns into crows and so on.

And there at the place of the big Bora you can see the trees standing tall and gaunt, sad-looking in their somber hues, waving with a sad wailing their branches toward the lake that now covers the place where the Bora was held. And it bears the name of Googoorewon, the place of trees, and around the edge of it are still to be seen the remains of the Bora ring of earth. And it is known as a great place of meeting for the birds that bear the names of the tribes of old. The Baiamul sail proudly about; the pelicans, their water rivals in point of size and beauty; the ducks and many others too numerous to mention. The Oo-boon, or blue-tongued lizards, glide in and out through the grass. Now and then is heard the "oom, oom, oom" of the Du-mer, or pigeons, and occasionally a cry from the bird Millin-dulu-nubba of "goo gool gai ya, goo gool gai ya."

And in answer comes the wailing of the gloomy-looking belah trees, and then a rustling "shirr" through the bibbil branches, until at last every tree gives forth its voice and makes sad the margin of the lake with echoes of the past.

But the men and boys who were at the place of the little Bora escaped the change. They waited long for the arrival of the tribes who never came.

At last Baiame said, "Surely mighty enemies have slain our friends, and not one escapes to tell us of their fate. Even now these enemies may be upon our track. Let us go into a far country."

And swiftly they went to Noondoo.

Hurrying along with them was a dog of Baiame's, which would rather have lain by the roadside than travel so swiftly, but Baiame would not leave her and hurried her on.

When they reached the springs of Noondoo the dog sneaked away into a thick scrub, and there were born her litter of pups—but such pups as surely man never looked at before. The bodies of dogs, and the heads of Piggi-billas, or porcupines, and the fierceness and strength of devils. And gone is the life of a man who meets, in the scrub of Noondoo, an eer-moonän, or long tooth, for surely will it slay him.

Not even did Baiame ever dare to go near the brood of his old dog.

And Baiame, the mighty wirinun, lives forever. But no man must look upon his face, lest surely will he die.

So, alone in a thick scrub, on one of the Noondoo ridges, lives this old man, Baiame, the mightiest of all wirinuns.

The Goodoo of Wirreebilla

BAIAME and one of his sons were fishing in the big water hole called Wirreebilla, in the Barwon River. They caught in their net an enormous goodoo, or codfish. They dragged it up the bank, took out its insides and made a fire.

They next took the liver and fat of the fish, placed it in a sort of bag they had taken out of the fish and put it on the fire to cook. The fish they hung on the big gum tree near which they camped.

When the liver was cooked Baiame started to eat it, his son sitting down watching him, hoping to get a share. But he was not given any and, though he was hungry, he did not dare ask for any.

At length he reminded his father that he was there by saying, "I will go and get a drink of water."

No response; so he went down the steep river bank. He felt very angry. Some time passed; he did not return. Baiame wondered what kept him so long, and at last went to the bank of the river after him. He saw no sign of him, but he noticed the water was rushing much more quickly than before, and the fish were jumping up in it as if something unusual were happening to them.

Baiame knew at once what it was. His son was angry, and being a great wirinun, or sorcerer, had determined to empty the great fishing hole by making all the water run away downstream, and the fish with it.

Even as Baiame watched he saw the water run faster and faster until the hole became visibly emptier. He was very angry with his son and, leaving the cod hanging on the tree, he went after him. He cut across the deep bends of the winding river, looking each time he struck the river to see that the water was ahead of him. He knew his son must be with the water.

He reached Brewarrina without overtaking him, and saw the water still flowing rapidly past. Below Brewarrina he knew of an underground channel. As he neared it he called out, "Go in under the earth with the water."

His son was indeed there, for he replied, jeering, "Go on! Into stone you will turn."

The son, though a great sorcerer, was powerless to resist his father, and was obliged to enter the underground passage. His father had blinded him, so that he could not see to avoid it. And when he was in it, Baiame pressed the earth down from above, keeping there imprisoned the remains of his son forever.

Baiame, having stopped the water from flowing away, retraced his steps to Wirreebilla.

The cod was still hanging where he had left it.

And there it still is, in the form of a fish, a huge dark lump on the bark of the tree to which it hung, and still known to the tribes as the Goodoo of Wirreebilla. And when the tribes tell its legend they say, "Baiame's son deserved death; he mocked his father. But his last words are true, for Baiame, away in Bullima, his sky camp, is partly turned into stone."

The Finding of the Eleänba Wunda

A MAN was trying to dig bilbas, or sand-hill rats, out of their burrows. He dug so deeply that he reached another world.

The opening he made was only a small one. He looked through it. He saw hideous monsters with feet having two toes each.

These monsters were so terrifying to look at that the man dropped his yam stick and swiftly retraced his way.

On emerging from the burrows, he saw Mullian the eagle-hawk. He told him what he had seen. Mullian made him go with him and show him where these monsters were. On reaching the opening, Mullian made it large enough to go through, which he did, commanding his companion to follow, who did so tremblingly. Boldly Mullian went up to the monsters and asked them of what tribe they were, he having seen none such before.

They told him, calling him by his name, which surprised him. They were, they said, the Eleänba Wunda, who had charge of all evildoers, whom they had to keep constantly moving and never allow to use their right hands.

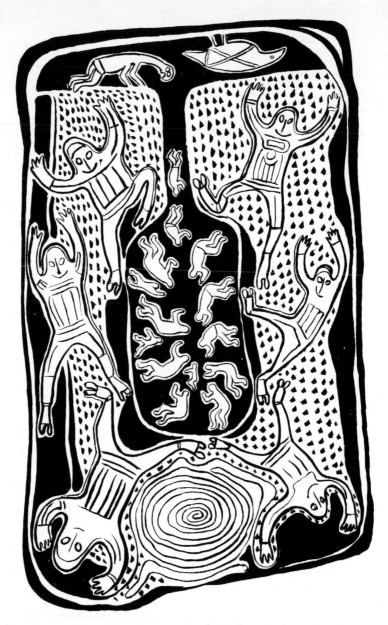

THE FINDING OF THE ELEÄNBA WUNDA

This is a pretty straightforward story. There in the corner is the man who dug the deep hole. Wahn the crow is looking the other way, but he isn't missing much. The two-toed monsters are poking round the poor spirits who didn't reach Bullima. The dots are not only here for "look-nice"; they are really the flames licking around them all.

The entrance of Mullian and his companion had so astonished the spirits undergoing punishment that some, for a moment, ceased moving. Immediately the Eleänba Wunda seized them and plunged them into a fire, of which there were two, one on each side of the cavernlike place.

Mullian's companion felt frightened. Thinking he too would be hurt in some way, he kept close to Mullian.

The Eleänba Wunda knew what he was thinking. One said, "Only those who deserve punishment are treated as you see. If a good spirit comes here we send him to Bullima; only the evildoers are kept here. You are the first living men who have ever been here.

"It is night in your country now; only the spirits are abroad. You must stay with us until it is light again up there."

Mullian knew it would be no good to attempt to go if the Eleänba Wunda wanted them to stay, so he took no notice of the signs his companion gave him to leave speedily.

The Eleänba Wunda offered them food. Mullian ate a good supper, but his companion would touch nothing. Nor, when they lay down to rest, did he sleep. He saw that all through the night the spirits were kept moving. Some were sent up to earth; these returned later, bringing new spirits which they had captured from the bodies of the lately dead. Those who had been evildoers were added to the throng of perpetual movers, their right hands beaten down if they raised or even moved them.

The next morning the Eleänba Wunda offered Mullian and his companion food; and Mullian ate, and again his companion refused.

After his meal Mullian said they would go. The Eleänba Wunda made no effort to keep them, so they climbed up the way they had come down.

As soon as they reached the top of the burrows, Mullian's companion made a fire and smoked himself and Mullian, lest they had brought some evil from this underground world.

His companion expected to see Mullian die from the effect of the food he had eaten there, but instead of sickening, Mullian seemed stronger than before.

So was the place of punishment discovered to the tribes by Mullian, one of the bravest of warriors.

The Babymakers

BAHLOO the moon was the maker of girl babies, in which work Wahn the crow sometimes helped. But it did not do for Wahn to be left to make them alone, for all the girl babies he made grew up to be noisy, quarrelsome women.

Bu-maya-mul the wood lizard made the boys, with sometimes a helping hand from Bahloo.

Bahloo and Wahn were both great wirinuns, and lived together.

One day Wahn said, "Suppose, instead of always making fresh babies to take their place, we give the dead people a chance, and let them come to life again. We could do it together."

"No," said Bahloo, "they are dead. The worst of them are burned by now, the bad ones are with the Eleänba Wunda, the good are in Bullima, or roaming where they please. Let them stay dead."

"But a great many have died lately—we shall have too few people on the earth if we let them all die."

"Never mind, make more babies. Let them die."

THE BABYMAKERS

Around the edge of this picture are the spirits who hold up the sky by standing all around the edge of it, and in the middle is the spirit who sits in the center of the sky holding the ends of the kurrajong-fiber ropes to which the earth hangs. Bahloo the moon is in his emu disguise, his two wives digging the grubs up all around him; also the little long-tongued wood lizard is there and, of course, Wahn the crow. The thing near Wahn is a branch of the spirit tree that carried Bahloo up to the sky when Wahn blew on it.

More than once Wahn tried to persuade Bahloo to join him in making the dead people live again, but Bahloo said, "Let them be. Their spirits may be in others by now. Let them be."

These repeated refusals made Wahn angry. One day he went off hunting alone. He came to a big gum tree where he saw a large number of Yulu-mara, or grubs. He went back to his camp.

He said again to Bahloo, "Well, have you thought better of it yet? Will you help me to make the dead live again?"

"No," said Bahloo. "Let them lie dead. Their widows can marry the young men."

Then Wahn told him that he had found a tree with quantities of grubs on it, and proposed that they should go out together and get as many as they wanted.

They went, and when they reached the tree Wahn said, "I will stay down here. You go up the tree, and hook the grubs out with this." And he gave him a midjeer, or stick with a barbed end.

Up went Bahloo, and with the hooked stick quickly fished out a number of grubs, which he threw down to Wahn.

Each time he did so, Wahn breathed on the tree, which at each breath grew higher and higher. Over and over again this happened until at last the topmost branches were near the sky. Then Bahloo noticed the height, and said, "Why, where am I? Where have I got to?"

Even as he spoke the tree went right into the sky. Bahloo looked down, and away below him on the earth stood Wahn, who called out, "Stay where you are up there. You would not help me to try and give the dead men a chance to live again. You can stay by yourself up in the sky. I can make the girl babies alone."

And there every night that the moon is shining, Bahloo and the tree can be seen.

Bahloo travels all across the sky to try and reach the earth again, but he has to change his form to do so, for his old enemy, Yhi the sun, keeps a lookout to prevent him.

Long, long before this Yhi had loved Bahloo and wished to marry him, but he said she had had too many lovers— she should never have him. This made Yhi so angry that her love had turned to hate. And when Bahloo was put up in the sky by Wahn, she told the spirits who hold up the sky by standing all around the edge of it that whenever Bahloo came near them they were to hunt him back. They must watch, she said, all the time while she, wrapped in her red kangaroo skins, slept. If they let Bahloo escape, she would knock down the spirit who sits in the center of the sky holding the ends of the kurrajong-fiber ropes to which the earth hangs. Then, down would sink the earth to a place of darkness, where they should go with it.

After this threat Bahloo found it impossible to escape, anxious as he was to return to his babymaking, for with only Wahn at that work the world would soon be full of noisy, shrieking women.

At last he thought he would try to get past the spirits in another form. He took that of an emu. The spirits thought he was Gowa-gay the sky emu, and they let him pass.

When Bahloo was safe on earth again, he went to his old camp. His dogs, not knowing him, rushed out barking furiously. He spoke; his wives knew his voice, and called the dogs off. Then he changed himself into his original shape. But he feared that the barking of the dogs might have drawn his brothers' attention to him—they, he knew, did not want him back, desiring his wives for themselves, for should he not return they had first right to them. He told his wives to put a log, which held a Mingga spirit, into their wurley, or shelter, cover it with an opossum rug, then sneak away with him to a bira, or whitewood tree, where he knew there were quantities of grubs, near which they would camp, certain of food.

They had scarcely left, when stealthily up toward the covered log came one of Bahloo's brothers, meaning to kill him. He swung his boondi, or club, around, and brought it down on the log with fearful force; once, twice, thrice he did so. Then he kicked the log, which seemed to kick him back again, and which seemed hard, not soft, as a body would. His foot felt tingling with pain. What had kicked him? he wondered. He seized hold of the opossum rug, pulled it off and saw nothing under it. (A Mingga, or spirit tree, has the power to make itself invisible, even moving invisibly away.) He looked around the camp—the women were not there—then, knowing Bahloo his brother was a wirinun, or clever man, he realized that he had been tricked.

Limping back to his own camp, he determined to track them all next day. But he was never able to find Bahloo, who, whenever danger threatened him on earth, just changed himself into an emu.

Bahloo and his wives had a great feast of grubs; then he went off to his babymaking. After he had made some little girls, his friend Bu-maya-mul, the little long-tongued wood lizard, joined him with some little boys he had nearly made. He tried to alter some of Bahloo's little girls into boys, saying that boys were best, for they were the stronger fighters and better hunters, but Bahloo said, "Do not do that. Better have some girls. The boys will want wives sometime."

Then together these two made a number of little boys

and girls, which when they were finished they sent to Walla-gudjail-wan, who has charge of the child spirits who are waiting to be born, or reborn, as earth children.

Walla-gudjail-wan is very fond of mussels, of which she collects great heaps, and if the children touch them she gets so angry that she puts them away. Then Walla-guroon-bu-an, another spirit kind to children, takes pity on them and promises them earth mothers.

Those spirits who have been children before, and died young, when asked by him to name an earth mother they will choose to go to, generally name the women who were their earth mothers before. To these Walla-guroon-bu-an sends them, to be reincarnated, or born again. Or if their own mothers were not kind to them, they mention other women whom on earth they liked, and to those they are sent. Such child spirits as never had an earth mother, or cannot remember her, and know no names of others, have to take their chances. Walla-guroon-bu-an sends them off to the earth to hide themselves in the long drooping branches of the coolabah trees.

The first woman who passes under the branch on which a spirit child awaits is chosen by that child for its mother.

When one of these tree spirit-children is born there is always a coolabah leaf in its mouth, which has to be taken out immediately, or the child will die and its spirit return to the tree it came from. If the spirit children are left in the trees long, they wail and become very unhappy. The old spirits take pity on them and to stop their wailing turn them into bahn, or mistletoe clumps, hanging from trees; the babies' blood makes the red bahn flowers.

Sometimes there are clear spaces under these drooping trees. These are said to have been swept by the spirits for the wirinuns to come and lie on and talk to them.

When Bahloo is late showing himself in the sky, the

blacks say, "Bahloo has been making girl babies; they take longer to make than boys."

They know when he is coming by the haze that precedes him. "Look," they say, "Bahloo is coming, there is his dust."

It is Wahn the crow who changes girls into young women, at which time they have to please him by saying aloud the cry of his tribe, "Wah! Wah! Wah!"

But Bahloo has influence over women's lives from their birth to their death.

The Mopoke and the Moon

MOOREGOO the mopoke had camped away by himself for a long time. While alone he had made a great number of boomerangs, nulla-nullas, spears and opossum rugs. Well had he carved the weapons with the teeth of opossums, and brightly had he painted the inside of the rugs with colored designs, and strongly had he sewn them with the sinews of opossums, threaded in the needle made of the little bone taken from the leg of an emu. As Mooregoo looked at his work, he was proud of all he had done.

One night Bahloo the moon came to his camp, and said, "Lend me one of your opossum rugs."

"No. I lend not my rugs."

"Then give me one."

"No. I give not my rugs."

Looking round, Bahloo saw the beautifully carved weapons, so he said, "Then give me, Mooregoo, some of your weapons."

"No, I never give what I have made to another."

Again Bahloo said, "The night is cold. Lend me a rug."

"I have spoken," said Mooregoo. "I never lend my rugs."

Bahloo said no more, but went away, cut some bark and made a dardur, or bark humpy, for himself. When it was finished and he safely housed in it, down came the rain in torrents. And it rained without ceasing until the whole country was flooded. Mooregoo was drowned. His weapons floated about and drifted apart, and his rugs rotted in the water.

The Frog Heralds

WHEN Baiame ceased to live on this earth and went back the way he had come from Bullima, up the roundabout ladder of stone steps, to the summit of Oobi Oobi the sacred mountain, only wirinuns, or clever men, were allowed to address him, and that only through his messenger Walla-guroon-bu-an.

For Baiame was now fixed to the crystal rock on which he sat in Bullima, as was also Birra-nulu, his first wife. The tops of their bodies were as they had been on earth, but the lower parts were merged into the crystal rock.

Walla-guroon-bu-an and Kunnan-beili, Baiame's second wife, alone were allowed to approach them, and pass on their commands to others.

Birra-nulu, was the floodmaker. When the creeks were drying up and the wirinuns wanted a flood to come, they would climb up to the top of Oobi Oobi and await in one of the stone circles the coming of Walla-guroon-bu-an. Having heard what they wanted, he would go and tell Baiame.

Baiame would tell Birra-nulu, who, if she were willing

to give her aid, would send Kunnan-beili to the wirinuns, bidding her say to them, "Hurry to tell the Bun-yun Bun-yun tribe to be ready. The ball of blood will be sent rolling soon."

Upon hearing this, the wirinuns would go swiftly back down the mountain and across the woggi, or plains, below, until they reached the Bun-yun Bun-yun, or frogs, a powerful tribe with arms strong for throwing and voices unwearying.

This tribe would station themselves, at the bidding of the wirinuns, along the banks on each side of the dry river, from its source downward for some distance. They made big fires, and put in these fires huge stones to heat. When these stones were heated, the Bun-yun Bun-yun placed some before each man, laying them on bark. Then they stood expectant, waiting for the blood ball to reach them. As soon as they saw the blood-red ball of fabulous size roll into the entrance to the river, every man stooped, seized a hot stone and, crying aloud, threw it with all his force against the rolling ball. In such numbers and with such force did they throw these stones that they smashed the ball. Out rushed a stream of blood, flowing swiftly

down the bed of the river. Louder and louder rose the cries of the Bun-yun Bun-yun, who carried the hot stones with them, following the stream as it rushed past. They ran with leaps and bounds along the banks, throwing in stones and crying aloud without ceasing. Gradually the stream of blood, purified by the hot stones, changed into flood water. The cries of the Bun-yun Bun-yun warned the tribes so that they might move their camps onto the high ground before the water reached them.

While the flood water was running, the Bun-yun Bun-yun never ceased crying aloud. Even to this day, as a flood is coming, are their voices heard, and hearing them, the Daens, or blackfellows, say, "The Bun-yun Bun-yun are crying out. Flood water must be coming." Then, "The Bun-yun Bun-yun are crying out. Flood water is here."

And if the flood water comes down red and thick with mud, the Daens say that the Bun-yun Bun-yun, or flood frogs, must have let it pass them without purifying it.

The Firemakers

IN the days when Bootoolga the crane married Goonur the kangaroo rat there was no fire in their country. They had to eat their food raw or just dry it in the sun.

One day when Bootoolga was rubbing two pieces of wood together, he saw a faint spark sent forth and then a slight smoke.

"Look," he said to Goonur, "see what comes when I rub these pieces of wood together—smoke! Would it not be good if we could make fire for ourselves with which to cook our food, so as not to have to wait for the sun to dry it?"

Goonur looked, and seeing the smoke, she said, "Great indeed would be the day when we could make fire. Split your stick, Bootoolga, and place in the opening bark and grass, so that even one spark may kindle a light."

And hearing wisdom in her words, Bootoolga did as she said. And after much rubbing, from the opening came a small flame.

As Goonur had said it would, the spark lit the grass,

61

THE FIREMAKERS

Here is the great show that all the tribes put on to divert the attention of the man and woman who had discovered fire but who were selfishly keeping the secret to themselves. You can pick out the tribes line by line. Also you will notice that in one corner are the owl and parrot who did the secret work.

the bark smoldered and smoked, and so Bootoolga the crane and Goonur the kangaroo rat discovered the art of fire-making.

"This we will keep secret," they said, "from all the tribes. When we make a fire to cook our fish we will go into a binga-wingul scrub. There will we make a fire and cook our food in secret. We will hide our fire sticks in the open-mouthed seeds of the binga-winguls; one fire stick we will carry always hidden in our kumbi."

Bootoolga and Goonur cooked the next fish they caught, and found it very good. When they went back to the camp, they took some of their cooked fish with them. The blacks noticed it looked quite different from the usual sun-dried fish, so they asked, "What did you do to that fish?"

"Let it lie in the sun," said they.

"Not so," said the others.

But that the fish was sun-dried, Bootoolga and Goonur insisted.

Day by day passed, and after catching their fish these two always disappeared, returning with their food looking quite different from that of the others.

At last, being unable to extract any information from them, it was determined by the tribe to watch them. Bulooral the night owl and Ooya the parrot were appointed to follow the two when they disappeared, to watch where they went and find out what they did.

Accordingly, after the next fish were caught, when Bootoolga and Goonur gathered up their share and started for the bush, Bulooral and Ooya followed on their tracks.

They saw them disappear into a binga-wingul, or needle-bush scrub, where they lost sight of them. Seeing a high tree on the edge of the scrub, they climbed up it, and from there they saw all that was to be seen. They saw Bootoolga and Goonur throw down their load of fish, open their kumbi, or skin bag, and take from it a stick, which, when they had blown upon it, they laid in the midst of a heap of leaves and twigs. At once from this heap they saw a flame leap, to which the firemakers fed bigger sticks. Then, as the flame died down, they saw the two place their fish in the ashes that remained from the burned sticks.

Back to the camp of their tribes hurried Bulooral and Ooya, back with the news of their discovery.

Great was the talk among the blacks, and many the plans as to how to get possession of the kumbi with the fire stick in it, when next Bootoolga and Goonur came into the camp.

It was at length decided to hold a corroboree, and it was to be one on a scale not often seen, probably never before by the young of the tribes. The graybeards proposed so to astonish Bootoolga and Goonur as to make them forget to guard their precious kumbi. As soon as they were intent on the corroboree and off guard, someone was to seize the kumbi, steal the fire stick and start fires for the good of all. Most of them had tasted the cooked fish brought into the camp by the firemakers, and having found it good, hungered for it. Biaga the hawk was told to pretend sickness, to tie up his head and to lie down near wherever the two sat to watch the corroboree. Lying near them, he was to watch them all the time, and when they were laughing and unthinking of anything but the spectacle before them, he was to steal the kumbi.

Having arranged their plan of action, they all prepared for a big corroboree. They sent word to all the surrounding tribes, asking them to attend; especially they begged the Brolgas to come, as they were celebrated for their wonderful dancing, which was so wonderful as to be most likely to hold the attention of the firemakers.

All the tribes agreed to come, and soon all were engaged

in great preparations. Each determined to outdo the other in the quaintness and brightness of their painting for the corroboree.

Each tribe as they arrived gained great applause. Never before had the young people seen so much variety in coloring and design.

Beela, the black-cockatoo tribe, came with bright splashes of orange-red on their black skins. By contrast, the pelicans came almost pure white, only a touch here and there of black skin showing where the white paint had rubbed off. The black divers came in their black skins, but these were polished to shine like satin. Then came the Millias, the beauties of the kangaroo-rat family, who had their home in the morillas, or pebbly ridges. After them came the Bukkandi, or native-cat tribe, painted in dull colors, but in all sorts of patterns. Mai-ras, or paddymelons, came too, in haste to take part in the great corroboree. After them, walking slowly, came the Brolgas, looking tall and dignified as they held up their red heads, painted so in contrast to their gray bodies, which they considered too dull a color, unbrightened, for such a gay occasion. Among the many tribes there, too numerous to mention, were the parrots: the rose- and gray-painted Galahs, the green- and crimson-painted Billai. Most brilliant were the Billai, with their bodies grass-green and their sides bright crimson, so afterward gaining them the name of Crimson Wings. The bright little Gidgerigars came too.

Great was the gathering that Bootoolga the crane and Goonur the kangaroo rat found assembled as they hurried to the scene. Bootoolga had warned Goonur that they must only look on, and take no active part in the corroboree, as they had to guard their kumbi.

Obedient to his advice, Goonur seated herself beside him and slung the kumbi over her arm. Bootoolga again warned her to be careful and not forget she had it. But as the corroboree went on, so absorbed did she become that she forgot the kumbi, which slipped from her arm. Happily, Bootoolga saw it do so, replaced it and bade her take heed, so balking Biaga the hawk, who had been about to seize it; for his vigilance was unceasing, and, supposing him sick almost unto death, the two whom he was watching took no heed of him.

Back Biaga crouched, moaning as he turned, but ever keeping his eye on Goonur. And soon he was rewarded.

Now came the turn of the Brolgas to dance. Every eye but that of the watchful one was fixed on them as slowly they came into the ring. First they advanced, bowed and retired; then they repeated what they had done before, and again, each time getting faster and faster in their movements, changing their bows into pirouettes, craning their long necks and making such antics as they went through the figures of their dance as to make their large audience shake with laughter. They themselves kept throughout all their grotesque measures a solemn air, which only seemed to heighten the effect of their antics.

Now came the chance of Biaga the hawk. In the excitement of the moment Goonur forgot the kumbi, as did Bootoolga. They joined in the mirthful applause of the crowd, and Goonur threw herself back helpless with laughter. As she did so, the kumbi slipped from her arm. Then up jumped the sick Biaga from behind her, seized the kumbi with his kumbu, or stone tomahawk, cut it open, snatched forth the fire stick, set fire to the heap of grass ready near where he had lain—and all before the two realized their loss.

When they discovered the precious kumbi was gone, up jumped Bootoolga and Goonur.

After Biaga ran Bootoolga, but Biaga had a start and

was fleeter of foot, so outdistanced his pursuer quickly. As he ran he fired the grass with the stick he still held.

Bootoolga, finding he could not catch Biaga, and seeing fires everywhere, retired from the pursuit, feeling it was useless to try any more to guard their secret, for it had now become the common property of all the tribes there assembled.

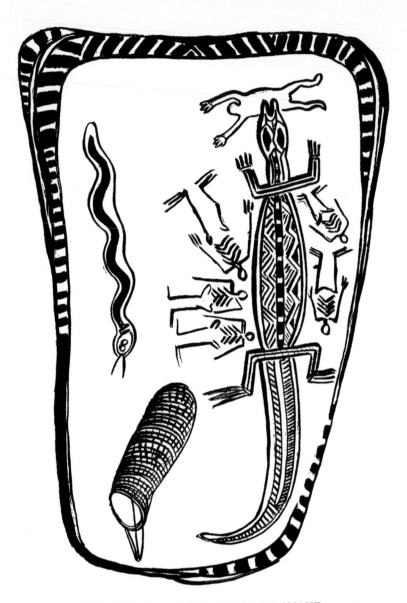

THE IGUANA AND THE BLACK SNAKE

*Here is the Iguana during its deadly days devouring a live Daen
and surrounded with the bones of other meals. The black snake
with his artful plan in mind is coming up for the talk. The poison
bag is drawn a little larger than necessary because of its importance
in the story.*

The Iguana and the Black Snake

W H E N the animals were first on the earth
they were very much bigger than they are now. In those
days the bite of a snake was not poisonous, but that of an
iguana was.

Mungoon-gali, the largest kind of iguana, which even
now in its dwarfed condition measures five feet or so from
tongue to tail, was, by reason of his poisonous bite, quite a
terror in the land.

His favorite food was the flesh of blackfellows, whom he
used to kill in numbers. Such havoc had he wrought a-
mong them that at last all the other tribes held a meeting
to discuss how best to check this wholesale slaughter.

The meeting was breaking up; the tribes could think
of no plan to save their relations, the Daens.

Just as they were dispersing, Ooyu-bu-lui the black
snake came to the watering place. He asked what the meeting was about. Dinewan the emu told him that Mungoon-
gali was so merciless toward the Daens, or blackfellows,
living almost entirely on their flesh, that they feared the
race would soon be exterminated if something were not
done to stop it.

"And," said Bohra the kangaroo, "though some of us are as big and bigger, as strong and stronger than Mungoon-gali, if we went to fight him he would kill us with the poison he carries in a hidden bag, and we too should die, even as our relations the Daens do. Most of us have relations among the Daens, and we do not wish to see them all killed, yet we know not how to stop the slaughter."

"I, too, have relations among them. My relations must be saved," said Ooyu-bu-lui.

"But how?" said the others. "We are nearly all their relations."

Mungoon-gali himself is their and my relation," said Moodai the opossum.

"But that does not stop him from slaying them, whether they are our relations or his—he slays all alike."

"I tell you that I shall save the Daens from Mungoon-gali," said Ooyu-bu-lui.

"But how?" again said the others in chorus.

"That I tell to none. But Yhi the sun shall not go to her rest tomorrow before I shall have that poison bag from Mungoon-gali."

"Yhi the sun shall not have hidden behind that clump of yaraän trees before you lie dead from the poison Mungoon-gali carries, if you fight against him."

"Did I talk of fighting? Is there no way to gain your end but by fighting? Let those who fight, die. I shall not fight him, and I shall live. No Mungoon-gali shall kill me."

So saying, away glided Ooyu-bu-lui through the trees surrounding the water hole where the tribes had met. Cunning, he knew, must be his guide to victory; not otherwise could he hope to win, for Mungoon-gali was bigger than he was, stronger, quicker of hearing and quicker to move; and, above all, the hidden bag of poison was his.

The only advantage that Ooyu-bu-lui thought he had was that Mungoon-gali had been invincible so long that he might have grown careless and unsuspicious. Ooyu-bu-lui decided he would wait until Mungoon-gali was gorged with his favorite food. He would then follow him until he saw him go to sleep after his feast. That would be the next day.

Having thus decided, Ooyu-bu-lui went near Mungoon-gali's camp and lay down to sleep there. The next morning he watched Mungoon-gali sally out. He followed him at a distance, saw him surprise three Daens one after the other and kill them all, then sit down and eat his favorite parts, taking some of the flesh afterward back to his camp with him. Ooyu-bu-lui followed him, saw him sit down and eat more, then roll over and go to sleep.

"Now is my chance," thought Ooyu-bu-lui, as he crept into the camp.

He was just going to raise his boondi, or club, to crack the skull of Mungoon-gali, when he thought, "But first I might as well find out where he keeps, and how he uses, the poison. If I had it I could soon make myself feared of all the tribes, as he is."

Thus thinking he sat down to wait until Mungoon-gali awoke. He did not have to wait long. Mungoon-gali slept but restlessly. Feeling something was near he awoke, sat up and looked around. At a little distance away he saw Ooyu-bu-lui.

As he was making a rush at him, Ooyu-bu-lui called out:

"Take care! If you kill me you will hear nothing of the plot the tribes have planned against you, of which I have come to warn you."

"What plot? What can the tribes do against me? Have I killed numbers of the biggest tribe to be frightened now of the others?"

"If you knew their plot you would have no need to fear them; knowing it not, your life is in danger."

"Then tell it to me."

"So I meant to do. But you were going to kill me though I had not harmed you. Why, then, should I save your life?"

"If you do not tell me I shall surely kill you."

"Then you will be killed yourself, for no one else will warn you."

"Tell me the plot, Ooyu-bu-lui, and your life is spared, and the lives of your tribe forever."

"How do I know that you will keep your word? You promise much, but how do I know that you will fulfill your promise?"

"Ask of me what pleases you, and I will give it to you, to show I mean what I say."

"Then while I tell you the plot that threatens you, give me your hidden poison bag to hold. Then only shall I feel safe. Then only shall I tell you what was planned at the water hole where the tribes meet to drink, where all said the Daens should be saved and your end assured. And surely it will be so if you do not know their plans."

Mungoon-gali asked Ooyu-bu-lui to name some other boon, and surely he would grant it, but his hidden poison bag he would give to none.

"That is the way. You ask me to name what I want. I do so. You cannot grant it. So be it. Keep your poison bag. I will keep my plot."

And he moved as if to go.

"Stay!" cried Mungoon-gali, who was determined to hear the plot at all risks.

"Then let me hold the poison bag."

Mungoon-gali tried to induce Ooyu-bu-lui to make other terms, but in vain, so he gave in. Reaching into his mouth he drew the hidden poison bag out; then he tried to frighten Ooyu-bu-lui from taking it by saying:

"The touch of it will poison one not used to handling it. I will put it beside me while you tell the plot against me."

"You will not do what I ask; I will go." And Ooyu-bu-lui turned away.

"Not so, not so!" cried Mungoon-gali. "Here, take it."

Assuming as indifferent an air as he could, Ooyu-bu-lui took the bag and went with it to his old place on the edge of the camp.

"Now quickly tell me the plot," said Mungoon-gali.

"It was this," said Ooyu-bu-lui, putting the poison bag into his own mouth. Then going on, "It was this. One of the tribes was to get this bag from you, and so take away your power to harm the Daens in the future. I vowed to do so before Yhi the sun went to her rest tonight. Not by strength could I do it. Nor by strength did I try to do it. Cunning I brought with me, and cunning has done it. Back I go now to tell the tribes."

And before Mungoon-gali had time to realize how he had been tricked, Ooyu-bu-lui was gone.

After him went Mungoon-gali, but his meal had been heavy; he only caught up with Ooyu-bu-lui in time to hear him tell the tribes that as he had said, so had he done.

"Give us then the poison bag that we may destroy it," they said.

"Not so," said Ooyu-bu-lui. "None of you could get it. It is mine alone. I shall keep it."

"Then you shall never live in our camp."

"I shall come as I please to your camps."

"Then we shall slay you. You are not big like Mungoon-gali."

"But I have the poison bag. Whosoever interferes with me, surely shall he die."

And away went Ooyu-bu-lui with the poison bag, leaving Mungoon-gali to tell the tribes how he had been tricked.

Ever since then the snakes have been poisonous, and not the iguanas; and there has been a feud between the snakes and the iguanas, who never meet without fighting. But though the snakes have the poison bag, they are powerless to injure the iguanas with it. For Mungoon-gali was a great wirinun, and he knew of a plant which, if eaten after snakebite, made the poison powerless to kill or injure. Directly an iguana is bitten by a snake he rushes to this plant, and, eating it, is saved from any evil consequences of the bite. This antidote has ever since been the secret of the iguana tribe, left in their possession by the Mungoon-gali who lost his poison bag by the cunning of Ooyu-bu-lui the black snake.

Weedah the Mockingbird

WEEDAH was playing a great trick on the blackfellows who lived near him. He had built himself a number of grass nunnoos, or humpies, more than twenty. He made fires before each, to make it look as if someone lived in the nunnoos. First he would go into one nunnoo and cry like a baby, then to another and laugh like a child, then as he went the round of the humpies he would in turn sing like a maiden, corroboree like a man, call out in a quavering voice like an old man, or in a shrill voice like an old woman. In fact he would imitate any sort of voice he had ever heard, and imitate them so quickly in succession that anyone passing would think there was a great crowd of blacks in that camp.

His object was to entice as many strange blackfellows into his camp as he could, one at a time; then he would kill them and gradually gain the whole country around for his own.

His chance came when he managed to get a single blackfellow into his camp, which he very often did; then by cunning he always gained his end and the blackfellow's death.

This was how he attained that end: A blackfellow, probably separated from his fellows in the excitement of the chase, would be returning home alone. Passing within earshot of Weedah's camp, he would hear the various voices and wonder what tribe could be there. Curiosity would induce him to come near. He would probably peer into the camp, and seeing only Weedah standing alone, would advance toward him. Weedah would be standing at a little distance from a big glowing fire, where he would wait until the strange blackfellow came quite close to him. Then he would ask him what he wanted.

The stranger would say he had heard many voices and had wondered what tribe it could be, so had come near to find out. Weedah would say, "But only I am here. How could you have heard voices? See, look around. I am alone."

Bewildered, the stranger would look around and say in a puzzled tone of voice, "Where are they all gone? As I came I heard babies crying, men calling and women laughing. Many voices I heard but you only I see."

"And only I am here. The wind must have stirred the branches of the belah trees, and you must have thought it was the wailing of children. You heard the laughing of Goo-goor-gaga, and thought it was the laughter of women; and mine must have been the voice of men that you heard. Alone in the bush, as the shadows fall, a man has strange fancies. See by the light of this fire, where are your fancies now? No women laugh, no babies cry, only I, Weedah, talk."

As Weedah talked he would keep edging the stranger toward the fire. When they were quite close to it he would turn swiftly, seize him and throw him right into the middle of the blaze. This scene was repeated time after time, until at last the ranks of the blackfellows living around the camp of Weedah began to grow thin.

Mullian the eagle-hawk determined to fathom the mystery, for as yet the blackfellows had no clue as to how or where their friends had disappeared. When Biaga, his cousin, returned to camp no more, Mullian made up his mind to get on his track and follow it until the matter was solved.

After following the track of Biaga, as he had chased the kangaroo to where he had slain it, on Mullian followed his homeward trail. Over stony ground he tracked him, and through sand, across plains and through scrub.

At last, in a scrub, and still on the track of Biaga, he heard the sounds of many voices, babies crying, women singing, men talking. Peering through the bush, finding the track took him nearer the spot whence came the sounds, Mullian saw the grass humpies. "Who can these people be?" he thought.

The track led him right into the camp, where Weedah alone was to be seen. Mullian advanced toward him and asked where were the people whose voices he had heard as he came through the bush.

Weedah said, "How can I tell you? I know of no people. I live alone."

"But," said Mullian the eagle-hawk, "I heard babies crying, women laughing and men talking—not one but many."

"And I alone am here. Ask of your ears what trick they played you, or perhaps your eyes fail you now. Can you see any but me? Look for yourself."

"And if, as indeed it seems, you only are here, what did you with Biaga my cousin, and where are my friends? Many are their trails that I see coming into this camp, but none going out. And if you alone live here, you alone can answer me."

"What know I of you or your friends? Nothing. Ask of

the winds that blow. Ask of Bahloo the moon, who looks down on the earth by night. Ask of Yhi the sun, that looks down by day. But ask not Weedah, who dwells alone, and knows naught of your friends."

But as Weedah was talking he was carefully edging Mullian towards the fire.

Mullian the eagle-hawk, too, was cunning, and not easy to trap. He saw a blazing fire in front of him, he saw the track of his friend behind him, he saw Weedah was edging him toward the fire; and there came to him in a moment the thought that if the fire could speak, well could it tell where were his friends.

But the time was not yet come to show that he had fathomed the mystery. So he pretended to fall into the trap. But when they reached the fire, before Weedah had time to act his usual part, with a mighty grip Mullian the eagle-hawk seized him, saying, "Even as you served Biaga the hawk, my cousin and my friends, so now I serve you."

And right into the middle of the blazing fire he threw him.

Then he turned homeward in haste, to tell the black-fellows that he had solved the fate of their friends, which had so long been a mystery.

When he was some distance from Weedah's camp he heard the sound of a thunderclap. But it was not thunder, it was the bursting of the back of Weedah's head, which had burst with a bang as of a thunderclap. And as it burst, out from his remains had risen a bird, Weedah the mock-ingbird, which to this day has a hole at the back of his head, just in the same place as Weedah the blackfellow's head had burst, and whence the bird came forth.

And to this day Weedah the mockingbird makes grass

playgrounds, through which he runs, imitating, as he plays, in quick succession any voices he has ever heard—from the crying of a child to the laughing of a woman, from the mewing of a cat to the barking of a dog.

Deegeenboya the Soldier Bird

D EEGEENBOYA was an old man, and getting past hunting much for himself; and he found it hard to keep his two wives and his two daughters supplied with food. He camped with his family away from the other tribes, but he used to join the men of the Mullian, or eagle-hawk, tribe when they were going out hunting, and so get a more certain supply of food than if he had gone by himself.

One day when the Mullians went out, he was too late to accompany them. He hid in the scrub and waited for their return, at some little distance from their camp. When they were coming back he heard them singing the "Song of the Setting Emu," a song that whoever finds the first emu's nest of the season always sings, before getting back to camp. Deegeenboya jumped up as he heard the song, and started toward the camp of the Mullians, singing the same song, as if he too had found a nest. On they all went toward the camp, singing joyously:

"Nurdoo, nurbber me derreen derreenbah, ah, ah,
  ah, ah, ah.
Garmbay booan yunnahdeh beahwah, ah, ah, ah,
  ah, ah.
Gubbondee, dee, ee, ee, ee.
Neäh neän gulbeejah, ah, ah, ah, ah."

This song roughly translated means:

"I saw it first among the young trees,
  The white mark on its forehead,
  The white mark that before I had seen only as the
    emus moved together in the daytime.
  Never did I see one camp before, only moving, mov-
    ing always.
  Now that we have found the nest
  We must look out the ants do not get to the eggs.
  If they crawl over them the eggs are spoiled."

When the hunters reached the camp, up came Dee-geenboya. The Mullians turned to him, and said:

"Did you find an emu's nest too?"

"Yes," said Deegeenboya, "I did. I think you must have found the same, though after me, as I saw not your tracks. But I am older and stiff in my limbs, so came not back so quickly. Tell me, where is your nest?"

"In the clump of the coolabahs, on the edge of the plain," said an unsuspecting Mullian.

"Ah, I thought so. That is mine. But what matter? We can share—there will be plenty for all. We must get the net and go and camp near the nest tonight, and to-morrow trap the emu."

The Mullians got their emu-trapping net, one made

of thin rope about as thick as a thin clothesline, about five feet high, and between two and three hundred yards long. And off they set, accompanied by Deegeenboya, to camp near where the emu was setting. When they had chosen a place to camp, they had their supper and a little corroboree.

The next morning at daylight they erected their net into a sort of triangular-shaped yard, one side open. Blackfellows were stationed at each end of the net, and at stated distances along it. The net was upheld by tall upright poles.

When the net was fixed, some of the blackfellows made a wide circle around the emu's nest, leaving open the side toward the net. They closed in gradually until they frightened the emu off the nest. The emu, seeing blackfellows on every side but one, ran in that direction. The blacks followed closely, and the bird was soon yarded. Madly the frightened bird rushed against the net. Up ran a blackfellow, seized the bird and wrung its neck.

Then some of them went back to the nest to get the eggs, which they baked in the ashes of their fire and ate. They made a hole to cook the emu in. They plucked the emu. When they had plenty of coals, they put a thick layer at the bottom of the hole, some twigs of leaves on top of the coals, some feathers on the top of them. Then they laid the emu in, more feathers on the top of it, leaves again on top of them, and over them a thick layer of coals, and lastly they covered all with earth.

It would be several hours in cooking, so Deegeenboya said, "I will stay and cook the emu; you young fellows take your mooroons and try and get some more emus."

The Mullians thought there was sense in this proposal, so they took a couple of long spears, with a jagged nick at one end, to hold the emu when they speared it. They stuck a few emu feathers on the end of each spear and went off.

They soon saw a flock of emus coming past where they were waiting to water. Two of the party armed with the mooroons climbed a tree, broke some boughs and put these thickly beneath them, so as to screen themselves from the emus. Then as the emus came near to the men, they dangled down their spears, letting the emu feathers on the ends wave to and fro. The emus, seeing the feathers, were curious as to how they got there, and came over, craning their necks and sniffing right underneath the spears. The blackfellows tightly grasped the mooroons and drove them with force into the two emus they had picked. One emu dropped dead at once. The other ran with the spear in it for a short distance, but the blackfellow was quickly after it, and soon caught and killed it outright. Then, carrying the dead birds, back they went to where Deegeenboya was cooking the other emu. They cooked the two they had brought, and then all started for the camp in great spirits at their successful chase. They began throwing their mooroolas, or waddies, as they went along, and playing with their bubberas, or returning boomerangs.

Old Deegeenboya said, "Here, give me the emus to carry, and then you will be free to have a really good game with your mooroolas and bubberas, and see who is the best man."

They gave him the emus, and on they went, some throwing mooroolas, and some showing their skill with bubberas.

Presently Deegeenboya sat down. They thought he was just resting for a few minutes, so ran on laughing and playing, each good throw leading to another effort, for none liked owning himself beaten while he had a mooroola left. As they got farther away they noticed Deegeenboya was still sitting down, so they called out to him to know what was the matter.

"All right," he answered, "only having a rest. Shall come on in a minute."

So on they went.

When they were quite out of sight, Deegeenboya jumped up quickly, took up the emus and made for an opening in the ground at a little distance.

This opening was the door of the underground home of the Murga Muggai spider—the opening was a neat covering, like a trap door. Down through this Deegeenboya went, taking the emus with him, knowing there was another exit at some distance, out of which he could come up quite near his home, for it was the way he often took after hunting.

The Mullians went home and waited, but no sign of Deegeenboya. Then back on their tracks they went and called aloud, but got no answer, and saw no sign.

At last Mullian-ga, the wisest of the Mullians, said he would find him. Arming himself with his boondis, or clubs, and spears, he went back to where he had last seen Deegeenboya sitting. He saw where his tracks turned off and where they disappeared, but could not account for their disappearance, as he did not notice the neat little trap door of the Murga Muggai. But Mullian-ga hunted around, determined to scour the bush until he found Deegeenboya.

At last he saw a camp. He went up to it and saw only two little girls playing about, whom he knew were the daughters of Deegeenboya.

"Where is your father?" he asked them.

"Out hunting," they said.

"Which way does he come home?"

"Our father comes home out of this." And they showed him the spiders' trap door.

"Where are your mothers?"

"Our mothers are out getting honey and yams." And off ran the little girls to a leaning tree on which they played, running up its bent trunk.

Mullian-ga went and stood where the trunk was highest from the ground and said, "Now, little girls, run up to here and jump, and I will catch you. Jump one at a time."

Off jumped one of the girls toward his outstretched arms, which as she came toward him he dropped, and, stepping aside, let her come with her full force to the ground, where she lay dead.

Then he called to the other child on the tree, "Come, jump. Your sister came too quickly. Wait till I call, then jump."

"No, I am afraid."

"Come on, I will be ready this time. Now come."

"I am afraid."

"Come on, I am strong." And he smiled kindly at the child, who, hesitating no longer, jumped toward his arms, only to meet her sister's fate.

"Now," said Mullian-ga, "here come the two wives. I must silence them, or when they see the children their cries will warn their husband if he is within earshot."

So he sneaked behind a tree, and as the two wives passed he struck them dead with his spears.

Then he went to the trap door that the children had shown him, and sat down to wait for the coming of Dee-geenboya. He had not long to wait. The trap door was pushed up and out came a cooked emu, which Mullian-ga caught hold of and laid on one side. Deegeenboya thought it was the girls taking it, as they had watched for his coming and done so before. He pushed up another, which Mullian-ga took, then a third, and lastly came up himself, to find Mullian-ga confronting him, spear and boondi in hand.

He started back, but the trap door was shut behind him, and Mullian-ga barred his escape in front.

"Ah," said Mullian-ga, "you stole our food and now you shall die. I've killed your children."

Deegeenboya looked wildly around and seeing the dead bodies of his girls beneath the leaning tree, he groaned aloud.

"And," went on Mullian-ga, "I've killed your wives."

Deegeenboya raised his head and again looked wildly around, and there, on their homeward path, he saw his dead wives.

Then he called aloud, "Here, Mullian-ga, are your emus. Take them and spare me. I shall steal no more, for I myself want little, but my children and my wives hungered. I but stole for them. Spare me, I pray you. I am old, I shall not live long. Spare me."

"Not so," said Mullian-ga. "No man lives to steal twice from a Mullian." And, so saying, he speared Deegeenboya where he stood.

Then he lifted up the emus and, carrying them with him, went swiftly back to his camp.

And merry was the supper that night when the Mullians ate the emus, and Mullian-ga told the story of his search and slaughter. And proud were the Mullians of the prowess and cunning of their great man.

Mullian-ga the Morning Star

MULLIAN the eagle-hawk built himself a home high in a yaraän, or white gum tree. There he lived apart from his tribe, with Moodai the opossum, his wife, and Moodai the opossum, his mother-in-law. With them too was Butterga, a daughter of the Buggoo, or flying-squirrel tribe. Butterga was a friend of Moodai the wife of Mullian, and a distant cousin to the Moodai tribe.

Mullian the eagle-hawk was a cannibal. That was the reason of his living apart from the other blacks. In order to satisfy his cannibal cravings he used to sally forth with a big spear, about four times as big as an ordinary spear. If he found a blackfellow hunting alone he would kill him and take his body up to the house in the tree. There the Moodai and Butterga would cook it, and all of them would eat the flesh; for the women as well as Mullian were cannibals.

This went on for some time, until at last so many blackfellows were slain that their friends determined to find out what had become of them, and they tracked the last one they missed.

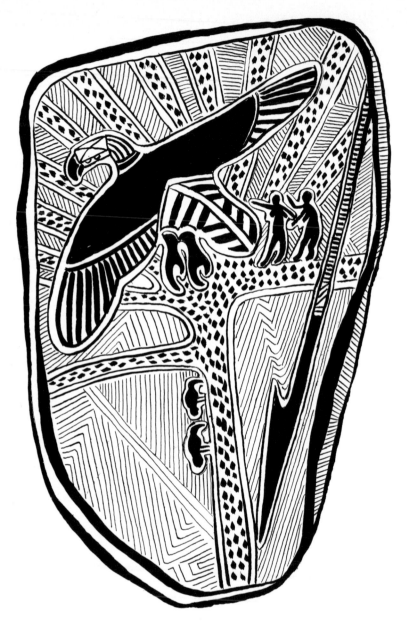

MULLIAN-GA, THE MORNING STAR

*This is all plain sailing: Mullian-ga the eagle-hawk, his two wives
up the tree, his enormous spear and the woodpeckers camping halfway up the tree on the first night.*

They tracked him to where he had evidently been slain. They then took up the tracks of his slayer, and followed them right to the foot of the yaraän tree, in which was built the home of Mullian. They tried to climb the tree, but it was high and straight, and they gave up the attempt after many efforts. In their despair at their failure they thought of the Bibbis, or woodpeckers, a tribe noted for its climbing powers. They summoned two young Bibbis to their aid. One came, bringing with him his friend Murra-wunda, of the climbing-rat tribe.

Having heard what the blacks wanted them to do, these famous climbers went to the yaraän tree and made a start at once. There was only light enough that first night for them to reach a fork in the tree about halfway up. There they camped, watched Mullian go away in the morning and then climbed on.

At last they reached the home of Mullian. They watched their chance and then sneaked into his humpy.

When they were safely inside they hastened to hide a smoldering stick in one end of the humpy, taking care they were not seen by any of the women. Then they went quietly down again, no one the wiser of their coming or going.

During the day the women heard sometimes a crackling noise, as of burning, but looking around they saw nothing. As their own fire was safe, they took no notice, thinking it might have been caused by some grass having fallen into their fire.

After their descent from having hidden the smoldering fire stick, Bibbi and Murra-wunda found the blacks and told them what they had done. Hearing that the plan was to burn out Mullian, and fearing that the tree might fall, they all moved to some little distance, there to watch and wait for the end. Great was their joy at the thought that at last their enemy was circumvented. And proud were Bibbi and Murra-wunda as the blackfellows praised their valor.

After dinnertime Mullian came back. When he reached the entrance to his house, he put down his big spear outside. Then he went in and threw himself down to rest, for long had he walked, and little had he gained.

In a few minutes he heard his big spear fall down. He jumped up and stuck it in its place again. He had no sooner thrown himself down than again he heard it fall. Once more he rose and replaced it. As he reached his resting place again, out burst a flame of fire from the end of his humpy.

He called out to the three women, who were cooking, and they rushed to help him extinguish the flames.

But in spite of their efforts the fire only blazed the brighter. Mullian's arm was burned off. The Moodai had their feet burned, and Butterga was badly burned too.

Seeing they were helpless against the fire, they turned to leave the humpy to its fate, and make good their own escape. But they left it too late. As they turned to descend the tree, the roof of the humpy fell on them. And all that remained when the fire ceased were the charred bones of the dwellers in the yaraän tree.

That was all that the blacks found of their enemies. But legend says that Mullian the eagle-hawk lives in the sky as Mullian-ga the morning star, on one side of which is a little star, which is his one arm; on the other a larger star, which is Moodai the opossum, his wife.

Wahn the Crow Wirinun

WAHN was as cunning as fifty cunning crows in one. That at least is what Wahn thought about himself.

One day he went fishing; he caught a very small codfish. He put it into a little water hole, intending to leave it there for some days, so that he could get it when he wanted it.

But Ga-ra-ga the blue crane and his two sons came along, and seeing a nice fat cod—for by this time the fish had grown—they caught it, killed it, split it down the middle and hung it on a tree to drain, before cooking it.

Wahn came along, saw the codfish hanging there and thought at once it must be his. He lay down to sleep in order that his Mullee Mullee, or dream spirit, might go and see if his fish were in the hole; if not, this must be his, though bigger than when he left it.

The wirinuns, or clever men, make great use of their Mullee Mullees, which, as soon as they've gone to sleep, they can order off anywhere they please, to do anything they wish to have done.

Wahn's Mullee Mullee came back and said it was his fish.

Then Wahn woke up and looked around. The fish was gone from the tree. While Wahn slept Ga-ra-ga had cooked it.

When Ga-ra-ga saw Wahn looking at his fish, he said, "Will you have some?" and politely offered him the back of the fish, which he thought was the best part.

"No," said Wahn.

All the more for us, thought Ga-ra-ga and his sons. And so they ate it all themselves, except the head, which they put on one side. Then they went to sleep. Going a little way off, Wahn lay down to sleep too.

Just at break of day he sneaked up with a boogoo, or long club, to Ga-ra-ga's camp. Ga-ra-ga was asleep on his back, his heels drawn up, and his knees sticking out. Wahn hit him with the boogoo across the knees.

Ga-ra-ga cried out, "Who hit me?"

Hearing him, his sons jumped up and looked about to see who could have hit their father. They saw no one, so ran over to Wahn's camp. But he was asleep. They woke him, and asked if he had heard anyone about, or if he had hit their father.

"No," Wahn said. "I was asleep."

They were all very puzzled, and felt very uneasy. When the sun rose, Ga-ra-ga told his sons to cut a bark canoe, so that they could cross in it to the other side of the river.

They went and cut one off a big gum tree, and brought it to their camp.

Then old Ga-ra-ga said to Wahn, "We are going over to the other side. There is something wrong about this camp."

Wahn said, "I am frightened to camp here, too. I'll go with you."

One son carried the canoe to the river, the other carried the old father. When the canoe was launched, they put the old man in it.

Wahn said, "You boys swim ahead of us. I'll bring your father across in the canoe."

The boys swam over. While they were doing so Wahn got the codfish's head, sang a little charm song over it and put it in the edge of the water. Then he made a start.

In the middle of the river, which was rising, and had a strong current, Wahn upset the canoe. Seeing this, in jumped the two sons from the other bank to try and save their father. But he sank before they could reach him, and was swept away.

Then they said, "We will kill Wahn for drowning our father."

They turned and swam after him; he was swimming quickly toward the bank from which he had started. He reached it and ran to their old camp. Before he left the river, he picked up again the cod's head, and shaking it toward the boys, sang:

> "All come to harm
> Who steal from Wahn."

The boys tried to reach the bank, but the farther they swam the farther they seemed still to have to swim.

Wahn was a great sorcerer, and he it was who was making the river spread wider and wider between the boys and the bank he was on. All the time he kept singing:

> "All come to harm
> Who steal from Wahn."

At last the boys felt sure they could not reach the bank, and that Wahn was a sorcerer, so, fearing for their own lives, they turned and swam back to the other side, where they easily landed.

They never saw Wahn again, but they let all their tribe know what he had done, so that all would be his enemies.

Wahn went on until he came to another camp, laughing as he went along his queer "Wah! Wah!" laugh, which always meant mischief to come or mischief done. Sometimes when the wah-wah-wah-ing went on very long it meant a little of both, for as soon as Wahn had finished one piece of mischief, he liked to be thinking of what to be at next.

The next camp he came to belonged to Mullian the eagle-hawk, where he lived alone with his two wives.

Mullian said to Wahn, "Let us go fishing." And when they reached the river he said to Wahn, "You go into that hollow log in the water; there is a codfish in it. I will stand here with my dindi ready to drive it into the fish when you hunt it out."

Wahn went, but he found no codfish, so was just coming out at the other end where Mullian was waiting with his dindi, or pointed stick.

As soon as Mullian saw him, he drove the dindi into his chest. As Wahn felt the sharp pain he spread out his arms, and made a squalling cry of "Wah! Wah! Wah!" which has been the cry of his tribe ever since.

When he got clear of the log, he pulled the stick out of his chest, and before Mullian suspected his aim he drove it through him, pinning him with it to the bottom of the river, as he sang:

> "Wah! Wah! Wah!
> All who hurt Wahn
> Will come to harm."

Leaving Mullian there, Wahn went up to the camp, where the two wives were.

They said, "Where is your uncle, our husband?"

"He's still in the river."

They waited a while, then they asked Wahn again, "What is keeping him?"

"His dindi, I expect."

And so it was, but not as they thought.

Night came on, but no Mullian returned, and when his wives saw Wahn go and take possession of his camp they began to suspect that Wahn knew more than he said, and that Mullian was not coming back.

They said, "Did you kill him?"

He sang:

> "All who hurt Wahn
> Will come to harm."

Some time passed, and Wahn stayed on in Mullian's place. At last one day a mob of fighting men came along, determined to kill Wahn for having taken Mullian's camp.

Wahn stood up to stand his trial. The fighting men made ready to throw at him. They took up their boreens, or shields, also, to protect themselves; for although Wahn had no right to do so when on trial, he had snatched up some of Mullian's weapons, and the fighting men thought he meant to use them.

Shower after shower of weapons fell around Wahn, but not one hurt him. He was such a sorcerer that even the fighting men could not harm him. Seeing this they gave him leave to keep Mullian's camp and belongings, including his wives.

When all this was settled, Wahn said to the fighting men, "I have a good song. I wish some of you would make a dance to it. I have made a little one, but not much. I will show it to you."

They all sat around in a ring, Wahn in the middle,

beside a big Mingga, or spirit-haunted, magic tree, which was invisible to the fighting men. Only Wahn, the evil wirinun, could see it.

Wahn crooned to himself:

"All who hurt Wahn
Will come to harm."

Then he danced a few steps; then he stopped, saying, "When I cry 'Doomoo! Doomoo! Doomoo!' you must say it after me. 'Doomoo! Doomoo! Doomoo!' "

Every time Wahn said this the roots of the Mingga cracked; but the fighting men did not hear them, and kept on repeating the cry, as Wahn had told them, watching him dance all the time. Every few minutes he called again:

"Doomoo! Doomoo! Doomoo!"

And back the fighting men called, "Doomoo! Doomoo! Doomoo!"

Crack went the roots of the Mingga.

Hearing, after his last cry, one big warning crack, Wahn gave a long leap to one side, getting clear from the ring of fighting men.

Just in time. Down came the huge Mingga, waving out its branches, covering all the fighting men and Mullian's widows, and crushing them all to death. Only Wahn was left unhurt.

At the place where this Mingga was, the tribe of Wahn the crow gather all the birds together to have corroborees, the crows always keeping the Kwa, or last dance, of the series for themselves. The Bukkandis, or native cats, sing for the crows to dance to, and so furiously do the crows dance that the dust rises to the sky, turning, in the early morning, into a dense fog. On seeing this the blackfellows say, "The crows had their Kwa last night and the Buk-kandis sang."

When Wahn left the Mingga-tree camp, he traveled on until he reached another camp.

There he saw a little boy, who had no mother, just starting to eat a Mai-ra, or paddymelon. Feeling hungry, Wahn said, "Give me some."

The little boy answered, "No, I am hungry. We had no breakfast this morning."

Wahn crooned:

> "All who hurt Wahn
> Will come to harm."

And as he sang he came nearer and nearer, every now and then asking the little boy for some meat. But the boy kept saying, "No."

Wahn tried to snatch the last piece the boy had, just as he was putting it into his mouth, and as he did so he slipped in a magic stone, which the boy, not knowing, hastily swallowed with the meat. Soon he felt what he thought was a piece of meat stuck in his throat. He went down to the river to get a drink to wash it down, but it stuck fast. He began to cough and choke. He came back to the camp, where he rolled on the ground in pain. He felt as if the thing in his throat was growing bigger and bigger, almost stopping his breath. At last with a final choke he died.

Wahn sang:

> "Wah! Wah! Wah!
> All who hurt Wahn
> Will come to harm."

He covered the body with an opossum rug, then went off to dig a grave. As soon as he had finished this he went back to get the body and bury it. Coming toward the camp he saw the boy's father, Mullian the eagle-hawk, a brother of the Mullian he had killed. (Brothers have the same name.)

As the father came near, Wahn started crying as if in great grief. He said, "What made you leave your boy alone? Why did you not take him with you? He was big enough, he could walk. Now he is dead. Something must have bitten him."

When the father saw that his son was really dead, he began to wail. He threw away all the food he had brought home—he had no heart to cook and eat.

He went with Wahn to cut a bark coffin from the trunk of a tree. When it was cut they took it back and put the body in it, letting the bark sides lap over it. They then bound it around with ropes made from bark fibers.

That night they lay down each on one side of the coffin, both keeping their hands on it, that the spirits might not steal the body.

In the morning they painted the coffin red and white, and carried it to the grave, where Mullian said to Wahn, "That hole is not big enough. You must make it bigger."

Wahn did so.

Then Mullian said, "Now lie down in it and see if it is long enough."

Wahn did so. Before he had time to get up again Mullian lowered the bark coffin, and put it on top of him, then started throwing in the earth as quickly as possible until both Wahn and the boy were well buried.

That done, Mullian went back to the camp. He sat there thinking about his boy, and rejoicing that he had avenged him by burying Wahn, whom he had all along suspected of causing his death. Suddenly he felt that some-one was near him. He looked up. There, standing before him, he saw Wahn! Wahn, whom he had just buried deep in the earth!

Wahn smiled and sang:

> "Wah! Wah! Wah!
> All who hurt Wahn
> Will come to harm."

Then he turned and went away without speaking.

Unseen by Mullian, he watched him one day go out hunting. Then Wahn lay down to sleep and sent out his Mullee Mullee, or dream spirit, to try and kill Mullian. The Mullee Mullee saw Mullian climb a tree after an opossum. The Mullee Mullee broke the branch Mullian was on.

Down, with the limb of the tree to the ground, came Mullian, killed on the spot by the force of the fall.

And when the Mullee Mullee came back and Wahn knew what had happened, he started off again, singing as he went:

> "Wah! Wah! Wah!
> All who hurt Wahn
> Will come to harm."

The Rain Bird

Boogoo-doo-ga-da was an old woman who lived alone with her four hundred dingoes. From living so long with these dogs she had grown not to care for her fellow creatures except as food. She and the dogs lived on human flesh, and it was her cunning which gained such food for them all.

She would sally forth from her camp with her two little dogs; she would be sure to meet some blackfellows, probably twenty or thirty, going down to the creek. She would say, "I can tell you where there are lots of Mai-ras."

They would ask where, and she would answer, "Over there, on the point of that morilla. If you will go there and have your nullas ready, I will go with my two dogs and round them up toward you."

The blackfellows invariably stationed themselves where she had told them, and off went Boogoo-doo-ga-da and her two dogs. But not to round up the Mai-ras, or paddy-melons.

She went quickly toward her camp, calling softly,

"Birri gu gu," which was the signal for the dingoes to come out.

Quickly they came and surrounded the blackfellows, took them by surprise, flew at them, bit and worried them to death.

Then they and Boogoo-doo-ga-da dragged the bodies to their camp. There they were cooked and were food for the old woman and the dogs for some time. As soon as the supply was finished the same process was repeated.

The blackfellows missed so many of their friends that they determined to find out what had become of them. They began to suspect the old woman who lived alone and hunted over the morillas with her two little dogs. They proposed that the next party that went to the creek should divide, and some stay behind in hiding and watch what went on.

Those watching saw the old woman advance toward their friends, talk to them for a while and then go off with her two dogs. They saw their friends station themselves at the point of the morilla, holding their nullas in readiness, as if waiting for something to come. Presently they heard a low cry from the old woman of "Birri gu gu," which was quickly followed by dingoes coming out of the bush in every direction, in hundreds, surrounding the blackfellows at the point.

The dingoes closed in, quickly hemming the blackfellows in all around; then they made a simultaneous rush at them, tore them with their teeth and killed them.

The blackfellows watching saw that when the dingoes had killed their friends they were joined by the old woman, who helped them to drag off the bodies to their camp.

Having seen all this, back went the watchers to their tribe and told what they had seen.

All the tribes around mustered up and decided to execute a swift vengeance.

In order to do so, out they sallied well armed. A detachment went on to entrap the dingoes and Boogoo-doo-ga-da. Then just when the usual killing of the blacks was to begin and the dingoes were closing in around them for the purpose, up rushed over two hundred blackfellows. So successful was their attack that every dingo was killed, as well as Boogoo-doo-ga-da and her two little dogs.

The old woman lay where she had been slain, but as the blacks went away they heard her cry, "Boogoo-doo-ga-da."

So back they went and broke her bones. First they broke her legs and then left her. But again as they went they heard her cry "Boogoo-doo-ga-da." Then back again they came, and again, until at last every bone in her body was broken, but still she cried, "Boogoo-doo-ga-da." So one man waited beside her to see whence came the sound, for surely, they thought, she must be dead. He saw her heart move and cry again, "Boogoo-doo-ga-da," and as it cried, out came a little bird from it.

This litle bird runs on the morillas and calls at night, "Boogoo-doo-ga-da." All day it stays in one place, and only at night comes out. It is a little grayish bird, something like a weedah, or bowerbird. The blacks call it a rainmaker, for if anyone steals its eggs it cries out incessantly, "Boo-goo-doo-ga-da," until in answer to its call the rain falls. And when the country is stricken with a drought, the blacks look for one of these little birds, and finding it, chase it, until it cries aloud, "Boogoo-doo-ga-da, Boogoo-doo-ga-da." And when they hear its cry in the daytime they know the rain will soon fall.

As the little bird flew from the heart of the woman, all the dead dingoes were changed into snakes, many different kinds, all poisonous. The two little dogs were changed into Daya-minya, a very small kind of carpet snake, non-poisonous, for these two little dogs had never bitten the blacks as the other dingoes had done. At the points of the morillas where Boogoo-doo-ga-da and her dingoes used to slay the blacks are heaps of white stones, which are supposed to be the fossilized bones of the men she killed.

The Rainmaker Wirinun

THE country was stricken with a drought.
The rivers were all dry except the deepest holes in them.
The grass was dead, and even the trees were dying. The
dardurs, or bark humpies, were all fallen to the ground
and lay there rotting, so long was it since they had been
used, for only in wet weather did the blacks use the dardurs. At other times they used only bough shades.

The young men of the Noonga-burra murmured among
themselves, at first secretly, at last openly, saying, "Did
not our fathers always say that the wirinun could make,
as we wanted it, the rain to fall? Yet look at our country—
the grass blown away, no doonbur seed to grind, the kangaroos are dying, and the emus, the ducks and the swans
have flown to far countries. We shall have no food soon;
then shall we die, and the Noonga-burra be no more seen
on the Narran. Then why, if he is able, does not the
wirinun make rain?"

Soon these murmurs reached the ears of the old wirinun. He said nothing, but the young fellows noticed that
for two or three days in succession he went to the water

hole in the creek and placed in it a wilgu-wilgu—a long stick decorated at the top with white cockatoo feathers— and beside the stick he placed two big gubberas, that is, two big clear pebbles which at other times he always hid about himself, in the folds of his waywa, or belt, or in the band or net on his head. Especially was he careful to hide these stones from the women.

At the end of the third day the wirinun said to the young men, "Go you, take your kumbus and cut bark sufficient to make dardurs for all the tribe."

The young men did as they were told. When they had the bark cut and brought in, the wirinun said, "Go you now and raise with ant bed a high place, and put thereon logs and wood for a fire. Build the ant bed about a foot from the ground. Then put you a floor of ant bed a foot high wherever you are going to build a dardur."

And they did what he told them. When the dardurs were finished, having high floors of ant bed and water-tight roofs of bark, the wirinun commanded the whole camp to come with him to the water hole. Men, women and children—all were to come.

They all followed him down to the creek, to the water hole where he had placed the wilgu-wilgu and gubberas.

The wirinun jumped into the water and bade the tribe follow him, which they did. There in the water they all splashed and played about. After a little time the wirinun went up first behind one blackfellow and then behind another, until at length he had been around them all, and taken from the back of each one's head a lump of charcoal. When he went up to each he appeared to suck the back or top of their heads, and to draw out lumps of charcoal, which, as he sucked them out, he spat into the water.

When he had gone the round of all, he went out of the water. But just as he got out a young man caught him up in his arms and threw him back into the water. This happened several times, until the wirinun was shivering. That was the signal for all to leave the creek.

The wirinun sent all the young people into a big bough shed and bade them all go to sleep. He and two old men and two old women stayed outside. They loaded themselves with all their belongings piled up on their backs, dayoorl, or grinding stones, and all, as if ready for a move. Then these old people walked impatiently around the bough shed as if waiting a signal to start somewhere.

Soon a big black cloud appeared on the horizon, first a single cloud, which, however, was soon followed by others rising all around. They rose quickly until they all met just overhead, forming a big black mass of clouds. As soon as this big, heavy rain-laden-looking cloud was stationary overhead, the old people went into the bough shed and bade the young people wake up and come out and look at the sky.

When they were all roused, the wirinun told them to lose no time, but to gather together all their possessions and hasten to gain shelter of the bark dardurs.

Scarcely were they all in the dardurs and their spears well hidden than there sounded a terrific clap of thunder, which was quickly followed by a continuous burst. Lightning flashes shot across the sky, followed by instantaneous claps of deafening thunder. A sudden flash of lightning, which lit a pathway from heaven to earth, was followed by such a terrible clash that the blacks thought their very camps were struck. But it was a tree a little distance off.

The blacks huddled together in their dardurs, frightened to move, the children crying with fear, and the dogs crouching toward their owners.

"We shall be killed," shrieked the women. The men said nothing but looked as frightened.

Only the wirinun was fearless. "I will go out," he said, "and stop the storm from hurting you. The lightning shall come no nearer."

So out in front of the dardurs strode the old wirinun, and naked he stood there facing the storm, singing aloud, as the thunder roared and the lightning flashed, the chant which was to keep it away from the camp:

> "Gurri mooray, mooray,
> Durri mooray, mooray, mooray."

Soon came a lull in the thunder, a slight breeze stirred the trees for a few moments, then an oppressive silence, and then the rain in real earnest began, and settled down to a steady downpour, which lasted for some days.

When the old people had been patrolling the bough shed as the clouds rose overhead, the wirinun had gone to the water hole and taken out the wilgu-wilgu and the gubberas, for he saw by the cloud that their work was done.

When the rain was over and the country all green again, the blacks had a great corroboree and sang of the skill of the old wirinun, rainmaker to the Noonga-burra.

The wirinun sat calm and heedless of their praise, as he had been of their murmurs. But he determined to show them that his powers were great, so he summoned the rainmaker of a neighboring tribe, and after some consultation with him he ordered the tribes to go to the Googoorewon, which was then a dry plain with solemn, gaunt trees all around it—trees which had once been blackfellows, before the Bora of Baiame.

When they were all camped around the edges of this plain, the wirinun and his fellow rainmaker made a great rain to fall just over the plain and fill it with water.

When the plain was changed into a lake, the wirinun

said to the young men of his tribe, "Now take your nets and fish."

"What good?" said they. "The lake is filled from the rain, not the flood water of rivers. Filled but yesterday, how then shall there be fish?"

"Go," said wirinun. "Go as I bid you. Fish! If your nets catch nothing, then shall this wirinun speak no more to the men of his tribe. He will seek only honey and yams with the women."

More to please the man who had changed their country from a desert to a hunter's paradise, they did as he bade them, took their nets and went into the lake. And the first time they drew their nets they were heavy with goodoo, murree, tukki and bunmilla. And so many fish did they catch that all the tribes, and their dogs, had plenty.

Then the elders of the camp said now that there was plenty everywhere, they would have a Bora that the boys should be made young men. On one of the ridges away from the camp, that the women should not know, would they prepare a ground.

And so was the big Bora of the Googoorewon held, the Bora that was famous as following on the triumph of the old wirinun, the rainmaker.

The Dogs of Bahloo

BAHLOO the moon looked down at the earth one night, when his light was shining quite brightly, to see if anyone was moving.

When the earth people were all asleep was the time he chose for playing with his three special dogs. He called them dogs, but the earth people called them snakes—the death adder, the black snake and the tiger snake.

As he looked down onto the earth, with his three dogs beside him, Bahloo saw about a dozen Daens, or blackfellows, crossing a creek. He called to them saying, "Stop, I want you to carry my dogs across that creek."

But the blackfellows, though they liked Bahloo well, did not like his dogs, for sometimes when he had brought these dogs to play on the earth, they had bitten not only the earth dogs but their masters; and the poison left by the bites had killed those bitten.

So the blackfellows said, "No, Bahloo, we are too frightened; your dogs might bite us. They are not like our dogs, whose bite would not kill us."

Bahloo said, "If you do what I ask you, when you die

109

THE DOGS OF BAHLOO

Of course Bahloo's dogs are the snakes; the stream they want to
cross is between them and the distrusting Daens.

you shall come to life again, not die and stay always where you are put when you are dead. See this piece of bark. I throw it into the water." And he threw a piece of bark into the creek. "See, it comes to the top again, and floats. That is what would happen to you if you would do what I ask you: first, under when you die, then up again at once. If you will not take my dogs over, you foolish Daens, you will die like this," and he threw a stone into the creek, which sank to the bottom. "You will be like that stone, never rise again, womba Daens!"

But the blackfellows said, "We cannot do it, Bahloo. We are too frightened of your dogs."

"I will come down and carry them over myself to show you that they are quite safe and harmless."

And down he came, the black snake coiled around one arm, the tiger snake around the other and the death adder on his shoulder, coiled toward his neck. He carried them over.

When he had crossed the creek he picked up a big stone, and threw it into the water saying, "Now, you cowardly Daens, you would not do what I, Bahloo, asked you to do, and so forever you have lost the chance of rising again after you die. You will just stay where you are put, like that stone does under the water, and grow, as it does, to be part of the earth. If you had done what I asked you, you could have died as often as I die, and have come to life as often as I come to life. But now you will only be blackfellows while you live, and bones when you are dead."

Bahloo looked so cross, and the three snakes hissed so fiercely, that the blackfellows were very glad to see them disappear from sight behind the trees.

The blackfellows had always been frightened of Bahloo's dogs, and now they hated them, and they said, "If we could get them away from Bahloo we would kill them."

And henceforth, whenever they saw a snake alone they killed it.

But Bahloo the moon only sent more, for he said, "As long as there are blackfellows, there shall be snakes to remind them that they would not do what I asked them."

A Legend of the Flowers

AFTER Baiame left the earth, having gone to dwell in Bullima, the faraway land of rest, beyond the top of the sacred Oobi Oobi mountain, all the flowers that grew on the woggis, and on the morillas, and all the flowers that grew on the trees, withered and died. None grew again in their place. The earth looked bare and desolate with no flowers to brighten it. That there had ever been any became but a tradition, which the old people of the tribes told to the young ones.

As the flowers were gone so were the bees. In vain the women took out their wirrees, or bark dishes, to fill with honey; they always returned without any. In all the length of the land there were only three trees where the bees still lived and worked, and these the people did not dare to touch, for Baiame had put his mäh, or brand, on them, claiming them thus as his own forever.

The children cried for honey, and the mothers murmured because the wirinuns, or wise men, would not let them touch the trees of Baiame, which were sacred from all forever.

When the all-seeing spirit saw that though the tribe hungered for honey, yet did they not touch Baiame's trees, he told him of their obedience.

Baiame was pleased, and said he would send them something which, when the land was perished with a drought, should come on the bibbil and coolabah trees, giving a food as sweet to the taste of the children as honey.

Soon were seen white sugary specks on the leaves of the bibbil, which the Daens called goonbean, and then came the clear wahler, or manna, running down the trees like honey. It piled into lumps, which stiffened on the forks of the branches, or sometimes fell to the ground, whence the children gathered and ate it when they could not reach the branches.

The hearts of the people were glad as they ate gratefully the sweet food sent them. But still the wirinuns greatly longed to see the earth covered again with flowers, as before the going of Baiame. So great grew the longing that they determined to travel after him, and ask that the earth might again be made beautiful. Telling the tribes nothing of where they were going, they sped away to the northeast.

On and on they journeyed, until they came to the foot of the great Oobi Oobi mountain, which towered high above them until they lost sight of its top in the sky. Steep and unscalable looked its sides of sheer rock as they walked along its base. But at length they espied a foothold cut in a rock, another and yet another, and looking upward they saw a pathway of steps cut as far as they could see. Up this ladder of stone they determined to climb.

On they went, yet when the first day's climb was ended

the top of the mountain still seemed high above them, and even so at the end of the second and third day, for the route was roundabout and long; but on the fourth day they reached the summit.

There they saw a stone excavation in which bubbled up a spring of fresh water, from which they drank thirstily, and found it so revived them as to make them lose all feeling of weariness, which before had almost exhausted them.

They saw at a little distance from the spring circles of piled-up stones. They went into one of these and almost immediately they heard the sound of a gayandi, or bull-roarer, through which the voice of Walla-guroon-bu-an was heard. Walla-guroon-bu-an was the spirit messenger of Baiame.

He asked the wirinuns what they wanted there, where the sacred lore of Baiame was told to such as came in search of knowledge.

They told him how dreary the earth had looked since Baiame had left it, how the flowers had all died, and never bloomed again. And though Baiame had sent the wahler, or manna, to take the place of the long-missed honey, yet they longed to see again the flowers making the earth gay as once it had been.

Then Walla-guroon-bu-an ordered some of the attendant spirits of the sacred mountain to lift the wirinuns into Bullima, the sky camp, where fadeless flowers never ceased to bloom. Of these the wirinuns might gather as many as they could hold in their hands. Then the spirits would lift them back into the sacred circle on the summit of Oobi Oobi, whence they must return as quickly as possible to their tribes.

As the voice ceased the wirinuns were lifted up through an opening in the sky, and set down in a land of beauty; flowers blooming everywhere in such luxuriance as they had never seen before, massed together in lines of brilliant coloring, looking like hundreds of yulu-wirrees, or rainbows, laid on the grass. So overcome were the wirinuns that for some moments they could only cry, but the tears were tears of joy.

Remembering what they had come for, they stooped and gathered quickly handfuls of the different blossoms.

The spirits then lifted them down again into the stone circle on the top of Oobi Oobi.

There sounded again the voice of the gayandi, and Walla-guroon-bu-an said, "Tell your tribes, when you take them these flowers, that never again shall the earth be bare of them. All through the seasons a few shall be sent by the different winds, but Yarraga Mayra, the east wind, shall bring them in plenty, blossoms to every tree and shrub, blossoms to wave amidst the grasses on woggis and morillas, thick as the hairs on an opossum's skin. But Yarraga Mayra shall not always make them thus thick, but only at times; yet the earth shall never again be quite bare of blossoms. When they are few, and the sweet-breathed wind is not blowing to bring first the showers and then the flowers, and the bees can make scarce enough honey for themselves, then the wahler shall again drop from the trees, to take the place of honey until Yarraga Mayra once more blows the rain down the mountain and opens the blossoms for the bees; and then there will be honey for all. Now make haste and take this promise, and the fadeless flowers which are the sign of it, back to your people."

The voice ceased, then the wirinuns went back to their tribes—back with the blossoms from Bullima. Down the stone ladder, which had been cut by the spirits for the coming of Baiame, they went; across the woggis and over the morillas back to the camp of their tribes.

Their people flocked around them, gazing with wonder-opened eyes at the blossoms the wirinuns carried. Fresh as when they left Bullima were these flowers, filling the air with fragrance.

When the tribes had gazed long at the blossoms and heard of the promise made to them by Baiame through his messenger, Walla-guroon-bu-an, the wirinuns scattered the flowers from Bullima far and wide. Some fell on the treetops, some on the plains and ridges; and where they fell their kind have grown ever since.

The name of the spot where the wirinuns first showed the flowers and scattered them is still called Girraween, the place of flowers. There, after the bees of Baiame had made Yarraga, the spring wind, blow the rain down the mountain of Oobi Oobi to soften the frost-hardened ground, green grasses shot up, framing fragrant bright flowers of many hues. And the trees and shrubs blossomed thickly again, and the earth was covered with cool grass and flowers as when Baiame walked on it.

It is the work of the bees of Baiame to make Yarraga blow the rain down the mountain, that the trees may blossom and the earth bees make honey.

Gladly does Yarraga do the bidding of the bees, lighting the face of the earth with the smile of rain water, for are not the bees his relations?

And the messengers who come in the drought, bringing manna, are the black ants, who bring the goonbean onto the leaves, and the little gray birds called dulloora, who bring the wahler, or liquid manna.

And when they come the Daens say, "A time of drought is here, a great drought on all the land. Few are the flowers anywhere, and the grass seed has gone. But goonbean and wahler will go, and the drought will go, and then the flowers and the bees will come again, for so it has always been since the wirinuns brought the blossoms from Bullima."

Gheeger Gheeger the Cold West Wind

DURROON the night heron lived near a
creek in which was an immense hollow log; this he used
both as a fish trap and as a man trap. He was by choice a
bunna, or cannibal. The immense log was hollow and was
under the water. In the middle of it Durroon had cut an
opening.

When a Daen came to his camp, Durroon used to ask
him to go fishing with him, saying he wanted a mullaya,
or companion, for he was like a gundooi, one emu living
alone. He wanted someone to go to one end of the log and
drive the fish to the other, where he could catch them.

Seeing sense in this, the Daen would agree, and off they
would go, Durroon armed with his spear, to spear the fish
when they came to his end of the log, so he said. But as
soon as he had sent his mullaya off to the far end, he would
go along the log to the opening in the middle.

Unsuspecting treachery, the Daen would come through
the hollow log, driving the fish ahead of him. As soon as
he was under the opening, Durroon would drive his spear
swiftly into him, killing him on the spot. Then Durroon
would drag his victim out and, dismembering him, cook
him.

In this way many men disappeared mysteriously, until at length a clever crow wirinun determined to solve the riddle of their disappearance.

Wahn the crow went to Durroon's camp. Durroon asked him to go fishing with him, but first offered him some good fat goodoo, or cod, he already had cooked.

Wahn agreed, and when they had finished their meal Durroon proposed they should go fishing, but Wahn said, "I ate too much goodoo. It was very fat. I ate a great deal and must have a sleep first before I start."

"All right. Plenty of time," said Durroon, feeling sure of his man-flesh supper.

Wahn went to sleep that he might send his Mullee Mullee, or dream spirit, to find out what was the trap Durroon had in the creek. The Mullee Mullee soon found out all about the opening in the top of the log. Having done so, back he came.

Then Wahn, having learned all, woke up and said he was ready, so off they started. Durroon showed Wahn where to enter the hollow log, at the far end.

Now Wahn was a great wirinun whom Durroon had no power to hurt, so he fearlessly went in. Durroon waited until he appeared under the opening, then down went the spear, bringing yells of "Wah! Wah! Wah!" from Wahn, who nevertheless went on and came out at the other end with the spear.

"What made you do that?" he said, pulling out the spear from where it had stuck in him.

"I did not mean to spear you," said Durroon. "I thought it was a big goodoo."

"Well, come on, I have had enough fishing," said Wahn. "You might make a mistake again."

On came Durroon, thinking Wahn really believed it was an accident, but no sooner had he caught up with Wahn than he found himself speared in his turn, and fatally, as Wahn struck to slay.

About this time, Gheeger Gheeger the cold west wind had been blowing such hurricanes that the trees had been blown in all directions, and the crows' humpies scattered everywhere. "Now," thought Wahn, "I will catch Gheeger Gheeger and shut her up in this immense hollow log, but first I must dry the water from it."

This he set to work to do. Soon, one day when Gheeger Gheeger was tired out, after having blown down miles of trees, and cut the tribes with her cold blast, Wahn sneaked upon her and drove her into the hollow log, which he blocked up at both ends and also at the hole in the middle.

Gheeger Gheeger roared and howled, but to no purpose.

"You only go about destroying things. You shall stay where you are," said Wahn.

Gheeger Gheeger promised to be more gentle in the future if only he would let her out sometimes. For a long time Wahn would not trust her and kept her closely imprisoned, but after a while he let her come out occasionally, after she promised to blow no more gales.

Sometimes she breaks her word and blows destructively as of old, but Wahn quickly captures her again, and hurries her back to her log prison.

There are holes now in this log and the breath of Gheeger Gheeger comes through, so unless Wahn finds a new prison for her, one day she will burst forth, and then there will be such a gale as never blew across the western plains before. Gheeger Gheeger will blast with her breath everything that stands in her way as she rushes to meet her loved Yarraga, the spring wind which blows from Kumbooran, the east, and which had of old been accustomed to meet Gheeger Gheeger as she blew from Dinjerra, the west, warming, where they met, her cold with his own balmy warmth.

Twice a year the winds had all met, holding great corroborees and wild revelings.

After the big corroboree the winds parted, each to return to his own country, hoping to meet again in another few months to corroboree again.

Hence the unrest of Gheeger Gheeger in the hollow log, and her loud wailing that she could not break forth from her prison and rush to mingle her icy breath with the balmy one of Yarraga.

Bilba and Mayra

B I L B A the soft-furred sandhill rat was once
a man, and lived in a camp with Mayra the wind for a
companion. Mayra was a strange mullaya for a man, for
he was invisible. He could hold conversations with Bilba,
but much as he desired it, Bilba could never see him.

One day he said to Mayra, "Why do you not become
like me that I might see you?"

"I can see you," said Mayra.

"Yes, I know that you can, but I cannot see you, only
hear you. I know you are there because you eat the food
before you. You catch opossums, and get honey, but though
I go with you, following your voice, yet I can never see you,
and I long to see someone again."

"But I can see you, so I am all right."

"But I cannot see you, and I long to see someone again.
I must travel away somewhere and join others of my tribe.
If I could only see you I would not wish for a better mul-
laya."

"Well, I am off hunting now. Are you coming?"

"No, I will stay in the camp today."

Mayra the wind went off, and when evening was at hand he was not yet back.

Suddenly Bilba heard a roaring in the distance such as he had never heard before. Then he saw, where the sound seemed to be, a column of dust and leaves spouting up. "What sort of a storm is this?" he asked himself. "I never saw anything like it before. I will go up to that sand ridge behind our camp and make a hole in the soft ground, into which I will get, so that this storm cannot take me away in its fury."

Off went Bilba hard as he could to the soft sandhill, the storm roaring behind him. There he made a hole and buried himself in it until the wind storm had passed.

Up came the wind, tearing on to the ridge, whirling around the camp, sending the bark and boughs flying about. On, on he went around Bilba's hole; but that he could not shift, so howling with impotent rage as he went, Mayra passed on until his voice was heard only in the distance, and at length not at all.

After a time Bilba came out. He had been so safe and warm in his hole in the sand that he lived there ever afterward; and there he took his wife, when he found one, to live.

And to this day the Bilba tribe live in burrows in the sand. They still hear the voice of the old Bilba's comrade, but they never see his face, nor do they hear him speak any longer their language as of old, for so angry was he at Bilba's desire to see his face or leave him that he only howls and roars as he rushes past their camps. And never since have any of the tribes seen where he camps, nor does anyone know except the six winds that blow, and they tell the secret to none.

How Mussels Were Brought
to the Creeks

O N E day in the far past a Munggi-wurray-mul, or sea gull, was flying over the western plains carrying a mussel. Wahn the crow saw her, and wondering what she carried, chased her. In her fear at being overtaken she dropped the mussel.

Seeing it drop, Wahn stopped his pursuit and swooped down to see what this strange thing was. Standing beside it, with his head on one side, he peered at it. Then he gave it a peck. He rather liked the taste of it; he pecked again and again, until the fish in one side of the shell was finished. He never noticed that there was a fish in the other side too, so he took up the empty shell, as he thought, and threw it into the creek.

There this Munggi, or mussel, throve and multiplied, all those that followed her being as she was, one fish enclosed between two shells.

Not knowing that he had thrown a Munggi mother into the creek, Wahn determined to pursue Munggi-wurray-mul and get more. Away he flew in the direction she had gone. He overtook her some miles up the creek beside a big water hole.

Before she saw him coming he had swooped down upon her, crying, "Give me some more of that fish in two shells you brought."

"I have no more. Let me go."

"Tell me, then, where you got it, that I may get more for myself."

"They do not belong to your country. They live in one far away which I passed in my flight from the big salt water here. Let me go." And she struggled to free herself, crying piteously the strange, sad cry of her tribe. But Wahn the crow held her tightly.

"If you promise to go straight back to that country and bring some more I will release you. That you must promise, and also that when I have finished those you shall bring more, that I may never be without them again. If you do not promise I will kill you now."

"Let me go, and I will do as you ask. I promise my tribe shall help me to bring Munggi to your creeks."

"Go, then," said Wahn, "swiftly back, and bring to me here on the banks of the creek the fish that hides itself between two shells." And he let her go, turning her head toward the south.

Away she flew. Days passed, and months, and yet Munggi-wurray-mul did not return, and Wahn was angry with himself for not having killed her rather than let her so deceive him.

He went one day to the creek for a drink and, stooping, he saw before him a shell such as he had thrown into the water. Thinking it was the same, he took no notice, but going on along the creek he saw another and yet another. He cracked one by holding it in his beak and knocking it against the root of a tree on the bank. Then he ate the fish, and looking around for more he found the mud along the margin of the creek was thick with them. Then, not knowing that the mussel shell he had thrown away had held a fish, he thought Munggi-wurray-mul must have returned unseen by him, disappearing secretly lest he should hurt her.

Later he found that was not so, for one day he saw a flock of her tribe flying over where he was.

They alighted a little higher up, where he saw some of them stick the Munggi they were carrying in the mud just under the water. Having done so, on they flew a little farther to stick others, and so on up the creek. Having finished their work they turned and flew back toward the seacoast.

Wahn noticed that the Munggi came out of the water, and opening their shells, stretched out and uttered a low, piteous, muffled, mewlike sound. Making their way along the mud, as they went they cried for the Munggi-wurray-mul to take them back to their own country. But their cries were unheeded, for the sea gulls were far away.

At last they reached the Munggi which had been born in the creek. These, being stronger and more numerous than the newcomers, soon taught them to live as they did, only one fish in two joined-together shells; and so have all mussels remained ever since. For though from time to time, on the rare visits of the sea gulls to the Back Creeks, fresh Munggi are still brought, these, too, soon change as the others have.

The Daens cook mussels in the hot ashes of their fires, and eat them with relish, saying, "If it had not been for Wahn we should not have had this good food, for he it was who caused it to be given to us by Munggi-wurray-mul, the mussel bringer."

Dinewan the Emu
and Wahn the Crows

DINEWAN and his two wives, the Wahn, were camping out. Seeing some clouds gathering, they made a bark humpy. It came on to rain, and they all took shelter under it. Dinewan, when his wives were not looking, gave a kick against a piece of bark at one side of the humpy, knocked it down, then told his wives to go and put it up again.

While they were outside putting it up, he gave a kick and knocked down a piece on the other side, so no sooner were they in again than out they had to go.

This he did time after time, until at last they suspected him, and decided that one of them would watch.

The one who was watching saw Dinewan laugh to himself and go and knock down the bark they had just put up, chuckling at the thought of his wives having to go out in the wet and cold, to put it up, while he had his supper dry and comfortably inside.

The one who saw him told the other, and they decided to teach him a lesson. So in they came, each with a piece of bark filled with hot coals. They went straight up to Dinewan, who was lying down laughing.

"Now," they said, "you shall feel as hot as we did cold."

And they threw the coals over him.

Dinewan jumped up, crying aloud with pain, for he was badly burned. He rolled himself over, and ran into the rain; and his wives stayed inside, and laughed aloud at him.

Goolay-yali the Pelican

AT one time the Daens had no fishing nets, nor had they the stone fisheries which Baiame afterward made for them, the best model of which is still to be seen at Brewarrina.

In order to catch fish in those days they used to make a wall of polygonum shrub and grass mixed together, across the creek; then go above it and drive the fish down to it, catching them with their hands against the break, or wall. Or they would put these breaks across a mubboon, or small tributary of the main creek, as a flood was going down, and as the water ran out of the mubboon, fish would be caught in numbers in the break.

Goolay-yali the pelican, a great wirinun, was first seen with a net. But where he had obtained it from, or where he kept it, no one knew for a long while. When he wanted to fish he used to tell his children to go and get sticks for the ends of the net, that they might go fishing.

"But where is the net?"

"It will be here when you come back. You do what I tell you. Get the sticks."

Frightened to ask more, the children went to break sticks which Goolay-yali said must be of eurah, a drooping shrub growing on the banks of the creeks, or near swamp-oak scrub. This shrub bore masses of large creamy bell-shaped flowers, spotted with brown, beautiful to look at but sickening to smell. Where no dheal grew, this shrub was used in place of that sacred tree.

When the children brought back the eurah sticks, there on the ground in front of their father was the big fishing net, ten or twelve feet long and four or five feet wide. Beside it was a small smoke fire of boodha, or rosewood twigs, onto which Goolay-yali now threw some of the eurah leaves, and when the smoke was thick he held the net in it. Then, taking the net with them, down they all went into the water, where two men with the net—through the ends of which were the eurah sticks—went downstream to a shallow place. Here they stationed themselves one at each end of the net stretched across the creek between them. The others went upstream and splashed about to frighten the fish down to the net, in which some were soon caught.

When they had enough they would come out, make fires and cook the fish.

Every fishing time the tribe puzzled over the question as to how and where Goolay-yali had obtained this valuable net, and as to where he kept it, for after each fishing time he took it away and no one saw it again until they went fishing. His wife and children said he never took it to their humpy.

One day the children thought that when they were sent for the eurah sticks, some of them would hide and watch where their father did keep this net.

They saw him, when he thought they were safely out of sight, begin to twist his neck about and wriggle as if in great pain. They thought he must be very ill and were just coming from their hiding place, when all of a sudden he gave a violent wriggle, contorting himself until his neck seemed to stretch to an immense length. The children were too frightened at his appearance to move. They stayed where they were, speechless, huddled together, their eyes fixed on their father, who gave another convulsive movement and then, to their amazement, out through his mouth he brought forth the fishing net.

So that was where he kept it, inside himself. The children watched him drawing it out, until it all lay in a heap in front of him. Then down he sat beside it, apparently none the worse, to await their return.

The children who had been hiding ran to meet the others, and told what they had seen. They were so excited at their discovery that they talked much about it, and soon the secret hiding place of the net was a secret no longer; but as yet no one knew how it was made.

At last Goolya-yali grew tired of having to produce his net so often, for the fame of this new method of fishing had spread throughout the country. Even strange tribes came to see the wonderful net. He told the people to do as he had done, and make nets for themselves.

Then he told them how to do it. They were to strip off mooroomin, or noonga (kurrajong) bark, take off the hard outside part, then chew the softer part and work it into twine, with which they could make the nets. He himself, he said, only swallowed the fiber, and it worked itself up into a net inside him; but that was because he was a great wirinun. Others could not do so.

After that all the tribes made fishing nets, but only the tribe of Goolay-yali could work the fiber inside them into nets, which the pelicans do to this day, the Daens say.

And the Daens tell you that if you watch the Goolay-yali, or pelicans, fishing, you will see that they do not dip their beaks straight down, as do other fish-catching birds. The pelicans put their heads sideways, and then dip their long pouched bills, as if they were going to draw a net. Into these pouches go the fish they catch, and then down into their nets, which they still carry inside them, though they never bring them out now as in the days of Goolay-yali, the great fishing wirinun.

Goolay-yali gave all his tribe the deep pouches which hang on their long yellow bills, so that they might use them instead of the net which each carries inside him. Though these are very small compared to the first Goolay-yali's net, they are big enough to let the tribe still bear his name, which means "one having a net."

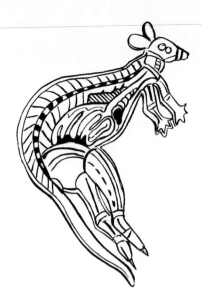

Bohra the Kangaroo

THERE was a time in blackfellow land when the night came down like a black cloud and veiled the world in darkness, letting neither moon nor stars be seen. But as Bohra the kangaroo liked to feed at night, he objected to this darkness, and being a great wirinun, he determined to put an end to it. So he just rolled the darkness back as if it had been a rug, and let it rest on the edge of the world, while the stars always, and sometimes the moon, shone out.

And very pleased he felt with himself when he was able to see to feed during the night and go about as he pleased on his four legs. For in those days Bohra the kangaroo went on four legs like a dog.

One night when he was feeding, he saw a number of fires ahead of him and heard a sound of many voices singing. Bohra was curious to know what this meant. Closer and closer he stole toward the place where the fires blazed and the voices sounded loudest.

133

He saw a long line of strangely marked figures come out from the darkness and go forward with slow steps to within the firelit circle. There they danced round and round, quickening their steps as louder and louder grew their voices, and faster and faster clicked the boomerangs.

At last with a "Hooh! Hooh! Hooh!" from the dancers the singing voices and the clicking boomerangs died away into silence. The figures stopped dancing, and disappeared into the bush. The fires were piled high again with broken wood, again the boomerangs were clicked, rolled-up opossum rugs thudded, and again the women's voices rose in chorus, as the long line of painted men came out once more from the darkness, to go through the same performance as before.

Bohra felt, as he watched them, a strong desire to dance, too. He reared himself on his hind legs, balancing himself with his tail, and jumped around the ring behind the last man. The singing stopped, the women shrieked, and shrieking pointed at Bohra.

The men turned and saw him standing on his hind legs, looking in wondering terror at the shrieking women.

Everyone seemed to be talking at once. Some said, "Kill him." Others said, "No. Let us see him dance."

The women were told to beat again the opossum rugs and start their singing, and as they did so, the men began to dance again. After them came Bohra, trying to do as they did.

The blackfellows turned to watch him. So funny he seemed to them that their anger quickly gave way to mirth. They laughed long and loudly as Bohra went solemnly, with a timid expression, hopping round, balancing himself on his tail, which left a snakelike track.

Leaving Bohra to himself in the ring, the men went away.

After a long interval they called to the women to start singing again. Then they came back, queer-looking figures indeed. They had made rough-looking tails of grass bound onto switches; these they had hung from the back of their waist belts. Round the ring they jumped as Bohra had done, their long tails waggling behind them. The women could hardly manage to go on singing when these queer-looking creatures danced before them, with their hands held as a kangaroo holds his forepaws.

When they stopped, an old wirinun said, "This Bohra has come to our corroboree without our asking him. He must be shown he had no right to do so, but we will not kill him, for he has shown us a new dance. But as he went after our dancers tonight, so forever shall his tribe move, jumping on their hind legs, and his forefeet shall be as hands, and his tail shall balance him. But before we let him go, we will make him one of us. He and his tribe shall be our brothers, and keep silent if they have seen our secret rites."

Then taking Bohra into the bush they knocked his canine teeth out. These teeth, the blacks say, his tribe have never had since.

At Bora, or sacred corroborees, the men of the Bohra tribe have ever since put on false tails and danced the kangaroo dance as when Bohra was bewitched into going on two legs, so starting a way of moving which all kangaroos have had to follow since; and this was how they learned to hop as they do.

Bohra Hunts the Dark

Bohra the kangaroo lived in a grass nunnoo with his wife Dinewan the emu. He was a great wirinun.

One evening when Bohra was lying down trying to sleep, Dinewan kept making holes in the roof of the nunnoo.

"What are you doing that for?" asked Bohra.

"Just for nothing," said Dinewan.

"Then get some grass and mend it up."

"There is no grass here."

"Then we will travel until we find some, for you won't let me sleep."

Off they went. It grew darker and darker every minute. Dinewan could not see where she was treading. She trod on bindias, which stuck into her feet and hurt her.

Limping along and feeling sore from the prickles, she said, "If you are such a clever man as you say, surely you could make the dark roll away! Hunt it right away to another country. Let me see where to walk. My feet are very sore. If you could hunt the dark away, then you would be a great wirinun. Oh, my poor sore feet!"

So crying she rubbed them against each other, which only made the bindias stick farther in, raising rough lumps on her feet. These lumps have been on the feet of her kind ever since, and their legs have been bare and hard up to the knee joint.

Now Bohra the kangaroo was really a great wirinun.

While it was still quite dark he said, "We will sleep here, and I will hunt the dark away while we rest."

They lay down.

As soon as Bohra was asleep he sent his Mullee Mullee, or dream spirit, out from his body to gather up the darkness and roll it away to the westward. Having done so, back came the Mullee Mullee to the body of Bohra, who now woke up and saw what his spirit had done.

He turned to Dinewan, whom he saw had slept with one eye and one ear open that she might see what he would do, and said, "My Mullee Mullee has rolled the night from us. The darkness is no more. It is rolled away forever from me. I and my people, from now on, shall be able to see to travel and feed at night as if it were day. For us there is no more darkness. You must feed in the daytime; I can, if I please, at night. You kept one eye and one ear open, you shall always sleep so. First one side of your head shall go to sleep and then the other, but never from henceforth both at once."

And since that time so it has been, even as Bohra the kangaroo wirinun said it would be.

The Galah and Oola the Lizard

O O L A the lizard was tired of lying in the sun, doing nothing. So he said, "I will go and play."

He took his boomerangs out and began to practice throwing them. While he was doing so a Galah came up and stood near, watching the boomerangs come flying back, for the kind of boomerangs Oola was throwing were the bubberas. They are smaller than others, and more curved, and when they are properly thrown they return to the thrower, which other boomerangs do not.

Oola was proud of having the gay Galah to watch his skill. In his pride he gave the bubbera an extra twist, and threw it with all his might. Whizz, whizzing through the air back it came, as it passed hitting the Galah on top of her head, taking both feathers and skin clean off.

The Galah set up a hideous, cawing, croaking shriek, and flew about, stopping every few minutes to knock her head on the ground like a mad bird.

Oola was so frightened when he saw what he had done, and noticed that the blood was flowing from the Galah's head, that he glided away to hide under a bindia, or

prickle bush. But the Galah saw him. She never for a
minute stopped the hideous noise she was making, but,
still shrieking, followed Oola. When she reached the bindia
bush she rushed at Oola, seized him with her beak, rolled
him on the bush until every bindia had made a hole in
his skin. Then she rubbed his skin with her own bleeding
head.

"Now then," she said, "you, Oola, shall carry bindias
on you always, and the stain of my blood."

"And you," said Oola, as he hissed with pain from the
tingling of the prickles, "shall be a bald-headed bird as
long as I am a red prickly lizard."

So to this day, underneath the Galah's crest you can
always find the bald patch which the bubbera of Oola
first made. And in the country of the Galahs are lizards
colored reddish brown, and covered with spikes like bindia
prickles.

The Wagtail and the Rainbow

D EEREEREE was a widow and lived in a camp alone with her four little girls.

One day Bibbi came and made a camp not far from hers. Deereeree was frightened of him, too frightened to go to sleep. All night she watched his camp, and if she heard a sound she cried aloud, "Deereeree, wyah, wyah, Deereeree."

Sometimes she would be calling out nearly all night.

In the morning Bibbi came over to her camp and asked her what was the matter that she had called out so in the night. She told him that she thought she heard someone walking about and was afraid, for she was alone with her four little girls.

He told her she ought not to be afraid with all her children around her. But night after night she sat up crying, "Wyah, wyah, Deereeree, Deereeree."

140

At last Bibbi said, "If you are so frightened, marry me and live in my camp. I will take care of you."

But Deereeree said she did not want to marry. So night after night was to be heard her plaintive cry of "wyah, wyah, Deereeree, Deereeree." And again and again Bibbi pressed her to share his camp and marry him.

But she always refused. The more she refused the more he wished to marry her. And he used to wonder how he could persuade her to change her mind.

At last he thought of a plan of surprising her into giving her consent. He set to work and made a beautiful many-colored arch, which, when it was made, he called Yulu-wirree. And he placed it right across the sky, reaching from one side of the earth to the other.

When the rainbow was firmly placed in the sky and showing out in all its brilliancy of many colors, as a roadway from the earth to the stars, Bibbi went into his camp to wait.

When Deereeree looked up at the sky and saw the wonderful rainbow she thought something dreadful must be going to happen. She was terribly frightened, and called aloud, "Wyah, wyah."

In her fear she gathered her children together, and fled with them to Bibbi's camp for protection.

Bibbi proudly told her that he had made the rainbow, just to show how strong he was and how safe she would be if she married him. But if she would not, she would see what terrible things he would make to come on earth, not just a harmless and beautiful roadway across the heavens, but things that would burst from the earth and destroy it.

So by working on her mixed feelings of fear of his power, and admiration of his skill, Bibbi gained his desire and Deereeree married him. And when long afterward they died, Deereeree was changed into the little willie wag-tail who may be heard through the stillness of the summer nights, crying her plaintive wail of "Deereeree, wyah, wyah, Deereeree."

And Bibbi was changed into the woodpecker, or climb-ing tree bird, who is always running up trees as if he wanted to be building other ways to the sky than the famous roadway of his Yulu-wirree, the building of which had won him his wife.

The Stone Frogs

A FAMILY of girls once so offended an old wirinun that one day when they were out hunting in the bush he turned them all into Yuaia, or frogs. When days passed and they did not return to the camp, their mother and relations thought that they had been stolen by men of a strange tribe.

Rain had come before there was any alarm about their absence, so all tracks were washed out, except the track of the Oodoolay, or round rainmaking stone, which had been abroad, as it always was, in muddy weather.

This stone had the spirits of past rainmakers in it, and could move about, as its tracks proved. Also, when it was making itself a new camp before rain, it could be heard laughing with joy in anticipation of the mud to come. No one was ever seen to touch the Oodoolay, yet its changes of camp were frequent.

Though some days had passed since they were missed, the mother of the girls still hoped to find them, thinking they might have seen the rain coming and built themselves a shelter in the bush, remaining there until it was over.

143

She went in the direction they had gone, and called aloud to them. There came an answering call. On she sped to whence it had seemed to come, and called again. Again came an answer from close beside her. She looked around, but saw no one. Again she called. There came an answer from a tussock of grass at her feet. Then she knew she had only heard the cry of Noora-gogo, the orange-and-blue beetle, which could always answer a Noonga-burra when one of that tribe was alone in the bush.

She gave up hope of finding her daughters, and being weak and hungry she looked around for food.

Soon she saw some tracks of Yuaia, or earth frogs, and finding where they were, she began to dig them out. Fine large Yuaia they were, the largest she had ever seen.

"What a meal I shall have," she said aloud.

There came a startlingly sad cry from the frogs, who seemed to be gazing fixedly at her.

But taking no notice, she went on, "I think I shall eat them here. I am very hungry, and if I take them to the camp the others will want some."

She stooped to pick them up, but such a crying came as surely never frogs made before, and so piteously they looked at her that she began to feel there was something strange about these frogs, and she dropped the one she held in her hand.

"But I am stupid," she said, "to take notice of a frog's cry. I would be mad to leave such a good meal here." And again she stooped to pick them up.

Again came their croaking cries, louder than ever. And the cries seemed to frame themselves into the words, "You must not eat us. You are our mother. We are the girls you lost. The old wirinun changed us into frogs because we but laughed at the mäh of his tribe, saying the back of it, the back of the emu, was humped as was his. You cannot eat us."

And loud was the croaking, and so frightened was the woman that she turned and sped quickly through the bush back to the camp with the mournful cry still ringing in her ears, and a vision of the piteous eyes ever before her.

She went straight to the old wirinun and said, "Did you change my girls into Yuaia, which are crying even now in the bush?"

"I did so," said he, quite proud the woman had seen the proof of his power.

"Why did you so? Why should you leave me to grow old with no daughter to care for me?"

"Did you not choose their father rather than me? Why should I think of you now? Let their father change them again. Surely he is more powerful than I am, since you chose him before me? I am but a humped-back one, so your girls said, even as they said was my mäh, the Dinewan. Well you must know that to scoff at the mäh of a man is to make war with his tribe, yet I war not. I but turn your daughters into such as have voices which none heed; no more can they scoff at the back of a Dinewan, my mäh. Go, woman, eat them. Yuaia is food that is good."

So he taunted the woman who once in her youth had scorned him.

"How should I, a mother, eat her young? What talk is this that you make? But alas! Surely another will find them and eat them. Only you can save them. Change them again, I pray you, so that none can eat them. Never again shall they scoff at a Dinewan. Never again will I scorn you. I will come to your dardur forever."

"Why should I take you to my dardur now you are old when you came not young?"

And he turned away, going on with the carving he was making on a boomerang, with an opossum's tooth.

"Change, oh, change them, I pray you, so that none

can eat them. I will give you the Doori, or grunting dayoorl, of my father's father's father to be yours forever.
No one but its rightful owner can use it, for does it not
grunt when a stranger touches it? This stone, which of old
belonged to the wirinuns of my father's tribe, I will give
you, this stone which alone of all dayoorls has a voice."

"Bring me the Doori," said the wirinun, "and I promise
to change your girls so that they shall never be eaten."

The woman brought the magical stone of her fore-
fathers, her greatest possession, which grunted as she laid
it at the wirinun's feet.

"Now go," said the wirinun, "into the bush, there you
will find your daughters, and find I have kept my promise.
Even now they are so that surely no one could eat them."

Back on her tracks went the woman to where she had
seen the Yuaia. Hopefully she went expecting to see her
daughters again. But when she reached the place there
were the frogs still.

"Oh, my daughters, my daughters! Shall I never see
you more as you once were?"

And she wailed aloud as if mourning the dead. But
no answer came from the Yuaia. Nor did they look toward
her.

Wailing, she stooped to pick one up.

"The wirinun tricked me," she said. "Surely indeed no
one will ever eat them, for they are turned into stone."

And so it was. Some were of plain gray stone, and
some with a stripe of green on them, just as the frogs had
been marked. Her daughters would be stone frogs forever,
as were the frogs that Birra-nulu and Kunnan-beili, the
wives of Baiame, had dug, and left for cooking before
they took that fatal plunge into the Corrigil Spring, whence
the Kurrias took them down the Narran, and whither
Baiame followed them, after changing the food they had

gathered into stones, to mark the spot forever. And there at the spring were the stone frogs still, as the mother knew, and now she saw their fellows in these the wicked wirinun had changed, these who had once been her girls but now were Yuaia Mayama, or stone frogs.

Maya-mayi the Seven Sisters

WURRUNNA had had a long day's hunting, and he came back to the camp tired and hungry. He asked his old mother for durri, or grass-seed cakes, but she said there were none left.

Then he asked some of the other blacks to give him some doonbur seeds that he might make durri for himself. But no one would give him anything.

He flew into a rage and he said, "I will go to a far country and live with strangers; my own people would starve me." And while he was yet hot and angry, he went.

Gathering up his weapons, he strode forth to find a new people in a new country.

After he had gone some distance he saw, a long way off, an old man chopping out bees' nests. The old man turned his face toward Wurrunna, and watched him coming, but when Wurrunna came close to him he saw that the old man had no eyes, though he had seemed to be watching him long before he could have heard him.

It frightened Wurrunna to see a stranger having no eyes, yet turning his face toward him as if seeing him all the time. But he determined not to show his fear, but go straight on toward him, which he did.

When he came up to him, the stranger told him that his name Mooroonu-mil-da, and that his tribe were so called because they had no eyes, but saw through their noses.

Wurrunna thought it very strange and still felt rather frightened, though Mooroonu-mil-da seemed hospitable and kind, for he gave Wurrunna, whom he said looked hungry, a bark wirree filled with honey, told him where his camp was and gave him leave to go there and stay with him.

Wurrunna took the honey and turned as if to go to the camp, but when he got out of sight he thought it wiser to turn in another direction. He journeyed on for some time, until he came to a large lagoon, where he decided to camp. He took a long drink of water, and then lay down to sleep. When he woke in the morning, he looked toward the lagoon, but saw only a big plain. He thought he must be dreaming. He rubbed his eyes and looked again.

"This is a strange country," he said. "First I meet a man who has no eyes and yet can see. Then at night I see a large lagoon full of water. I wake in the morning and see none. The water was surely there, for I drank some; yet now there is no water."

As he was wondering how the water could have disappeared so quickly, he saw a big storm coming up. He hurried to get into the thick bush for shelter. When he had gone a little way into the bush, he saw a quantity of cut bark lying on the ground.

"Now I am all right," he said. "I shall get some poles

and with them and this bark make a dardur in which to shelter myself from the storm I see coming."

He quickly cut the poles he wanted, stuck them up as a framework for his dardur. Then he went to lift up the bark. As he lifted up a sheet of it he saw a strange-looking object of no tribe that he had ever seen before.

This strange object cried out, "I am Bulga-nunnoo," in such a terrifying tone that Wurrunna dropped the bark, picked up his weapons and ran away as hard as he could, quite forgetting the storm. His one idea was to get as far as he could from Bulga-nunnoo, the bark-backed one.

On he ran until he came to a big river, which hemmed him in on three sides. The river was too big to cross, so he had to turn back, yet he did not retrace his steps, but turned in another direction. As he turned to leave the river, he saw a flock of emus coming to water. The first half of the flock were covered with feathers, but the last half had the form of emus, but no feathers.

Wurrunna decided to spear one for food. For that purpose he climbed up a tree, so that they should not see him. He got his spear ready to kill one of the featherless birds. As they passed by, he picked out the one he meant to have, threw his spear and killed it, then climbed down down to go and get it.

As he was running up to the dead emu, he saw that they were not emus at all but blackfellows of a strange tribe. They were all standing around their dead friend making savage signs as to what they would do by way of vengeance. Warrunna saw that little would avail him the excuse that he had killed the blackfellow in mistake for an emu. His only hope lay in flight.

Once more he took to his heels, hardly daring to look around for fear he would see an enemy behind him. On he sped, until at last he reached a camp, which he was almost into before he saw it. He had been thinking only of danger behind him, unheeding what was before him.

However, he had nothing to fear in the camp he reached so suddenly, for in it were only seven young girls. They did not look very terrifying; in fact, they seemed more startled than he was. They were quite friendly toward him when they found that he was alone and hungry. They gave him food and allowed him to camp there that night.

He asked them where the rest of their tribe were, and what their name was. They answered that their name was Maya-mayi, and that their tribe were in a far country. They had come to this country only to see what it was like. They would stay for a while and then return whence they had come.

The next day Wurrunna made a fresh start, and left the camp of the Maya-mayi as if he were leaving for good. But he determined to hide near and watch what they did, and if he could get a chance he would steal a wife from among them. He was tired of traveling alone.

He saw the seven sisters all start out with their yam sticks in hand. He followed at a distance, taking care not to be seen. He saw them stop by the nests of some flying ants. With their yam sticks they dug all around these ant holes. When they had successfully unearthed the ants they sat down, throwing their yam sticks on one side, to enjoy a feast, for the ants were thought by them to be a great delicacy.

While the sisters were busy at their feast, Wurrunna sneaked up to their yam sticks and stole two of them. Then, taking the sticks with him, he sneaked back to his hiding place.

When at length the Maya-mayi had satisfied their appetites, they picked up their sticks and turned toward their camp again. But only five could find their sticks, so those five started off, leaving the other two to find theirs. They supposed the sticks must be somewhere near, and that, finding them, the sisters would soon catch up.

The two girls hunted all around the ants' nests, but could find no sticks. At last, when their backs were turned toward him, Wurrunna crept out and stuck the lost yam sticks near together in the ground. Then he slipped back into his hiding place.

When the two girls turned around, there in front of them they saw their sticks. With a cry of joyful surprise they ran to them and caught hold of them to pull them out of the ground, in which they were firmly stuck. As they were doing so, out from his hiding place jumped Wurrunna.

He seized both girls around their waists, holding them tightly.

They struggled and screamed, but to no purpose. There was no one near to hear them, and the more they struggled the tighter Wurrunna held them. Finding their screams and struggles in vain, they quieted down at length, and then Wurrunna told them not to be afraid, for he would take care of them. He was lonely, he said, and wanted two wives. They must come quietly with him, and he would be good to them. But they must do as he told them. If they were not quiet, he would swiftly subdue them with his nulla-nulla. But if they would come quietly with him he would be good to them.

Seeing that resistance was useless, the two young girls complied with his wish, and traveled quietly on with him. They told him that some day their tribe would come and steal them back again. To avoid this he traveled quickly on and on still farther, hoping to escape all pursuit.

Some weeks passed, and outwardly the two Maya-mayi seemed settled down to their new life, and quite content in it, though when they were alone together they often talked of their sisters, and wondered what they had done when they realized their loss. They wondered if the five were still hunting for them, or whether they had gone back to their tribe to get assistance. That they might be in time forgotten and left with Wurrunna forever, they never once for a moment thought.

One day when they were camped Wurrunna said, "This fire will not burn well. Go you two and get some bark from those two pine trees over there."

"No," they said, "we must not cut pine bark. If we did, you would never more see us."

"Go! I tell you, cut pine bark. I want it. See you not the fire burns but slowly?"

"If we go, Wurrunna, we shall never return. You will see us no more in this country. We know it."

"Go, women, stay not to talk. Did you ever see talk make a fire burn? Then why stand you there talking? Go, do as I bid you. Talk not so foolishly. If you ran away, soon should I catch you, and, catching you, would beat you hard. Go! Talk no more."

The Maya-mayi went, taking with them their kumbus, or stone axes, with which to cut the bark. Each went to a different tree, and each, with a strong hit, drove her kumbu into the bark. As she did so, each felt the tree that her kumbu had struck begin to rise higher out of the ground and bear her upward with it.

Higher and higher grew the pine trees, and still on them, higher and higher from the earth, went the two girls.

Hearing no chopping after the first hits, Wurrunna came toward the pines to see what was keeping the girls so long.

As he came near them, he saw that the pine trees were growing taller even as he looked at them, and clinging to the trunks of the trees high in the air, he saw his two wives.

He called to them to come down, but they made no answer. Time after time he called to them as higher and higher they went, but still they made no answer. Steadily taller grew the two pines, until at last their tops touched the sky.

As they did so, from the sky the other five Maya-mayi looked out, called to their two sisters on the pine trees, bidding them not to be afraid but to come to them.

Quickly the two girls climbed up when they heard the voices of their sisters. When they reached the tops of the pines, the five sisters in the sky stretched forth their hands, and drew them in to live with them there in the sky forever.

And there, if you look, you may see the seven sisters together. You perhaps know them as the Pleiades, but the Daens, or blackfellows, call them the Maya-mayi.

Wurrunna's Trip to the Sea

WHEN the two Maya-mayi were lifted
to the sky from Wurrunna's camp, he, failing to recover
them, journeyed on alone.

He was now a long way from the spot he had started
from, which was near Nerangledool. He had passed Yaraänba, Narine, and had reached Nindeegoolee, where the
little sand ridges are, to where the eer-moonän, or long
tooths, had gone from Noondoo.

He was camping by some water when he saw a strange
creature coming toward him, having the body and head
of a dog, feet of a woman and a short tail. It bounded
four or five feet in the air as it came along, making a
whirring, whizzing noise with its lips.

"What is this coming to water?" said Wurrunna to
himself.

When the creature was close, he said, "It must be an
eer-moonän, one of the pups of the dog Baiame left at
Noondoo, that I have heard tell of."

He called out to it, "Where is your old master?" for
he thought he would find out if the strange creature knew
where Baiame was.

For answer the eer-moonän made the spluttering, whizzing noise with its lips that Wurrunna had already heard.

Wurrunna said, "Has he gone right away from you?"

Again came only the spluttering, whizzing noise, a sort of pursing of the lips together, and a blowing-out sound like "Phur-r, phur-r."

"Is it true that he has gone forever?"

"Phur-r, phur-r," came again the answer.

Wurrunna stood up and motioned the eer-moonän back, saying, "You go away now. That will do. I want you here no more. You tell me nothing of Baiame."

At the sound of the name "Baiame" the eer-moonän jumped away, saying as it went, "Phur-r, phur-r."

It quickly disappeared, going back to the sand ridges under which Wurrunna had heard that it and the rest of the strange litter lived, in huge caves, where they imprisoned any travelers they could round up into them. Nothing frightened them but mention of the name of Baiame.

Wurrunna did not mean to risk another encounter, so he hurried on to Dunger.

On, on he traveled for many days, until at last he reached Doogoober, which is on the sea. Seeing a wide expanse of water before him and feeling thirsty, he took his little bingui, or wooden dish, down to dip some out and drink.

"Kuh!" he said as he swallowed a mouthful before he realized the strange taste. "Kuh! Boodha! Boodha! Salt! Salt!" said he, as he spat out what he could.

He thought it must be the white froth that was salt, so he cleared this off with his hand, dipped the bingui in again, and again tasted.

"Kuh! Kuh! Boodha! Boodha! I am thirsty. I must go back to the water holes I passed and get a drink there."

Before going, he looked as far as his eye could reach across the sea. He said, "What sort of flood water is this that has a tree in it nowhere, not even a mirria bush, and is salt, salt to taste? It does not look like flood water at all. It looks like Goonagulla, the sky, with white clouds on it. Yet when the clouds move, the sky is still. All this moves and is water, though surely man never tasted such before."

Wonderingly, back he went to the water holes and quenched his thirst. Then he killed two opossums, and skinned them to make gulli-mayas, or water bags.

That night, as he camped out of sight of and some distance away from the sea, he heard its booming noise, for the wind had risen. What the noise was he did not know.

The next morning he went to see the strange water again, thinking he might now make out a bank on the far side. Seeing a high tree a few hundred yards from the beach, he climbed it and looked again seaward, scanning the distant horizon for trees or land. He saw only water, a dark angry-looking water that day.

"There is a thunderstorm in it. This must be the camp of Dooloomai the thunder, and the roaring winds," he said as he listened to the angry booming. "That is what I heard last night."

Then, as he saw the tide rising and the waves chasing each other onto the beach—where they dashed with an angry roar, going back only to come rushing in again higher next time—he said, "There must be Wunda, devils, in it, and they are trying to get me. I will go up that high mountain. There shall I see better."

But he climbed the mountain in vain. He saw only the strange water, as far as he could see. Water, only water.

Down the mountain he went again, back to the water

holes, where were hanging the opossum skins to dry. These he quickly made into water bags.

He waited until he saw the strange water as still as when he first saw it, then he went to it and filled the bags with it. He then picked up a few wa-ah, or shells, to take away with him. He meant to go straight back to his tribe and tell them what he had seen, taking with him the bags of water that they might taste it, and know his story was true.

On his return journey he met a very old Daen, or blackfellow. Wurrunna thought he might know something of this strange water and its booming voices. The old wiri-nun listened to all Wurrunna told him.

He tasted the water, spat it out again, sat silent for some time.

Then he said, "Surely then have my father's fathers spoken truly when they told their children that there was, beyond the mountains, more water than the eye of man has ever seen—water which is full of dangers for man, whom it pursues to its very edge, where it rages when it cannot catch him for the many monsters which live in it, and are bigger, they said, and deadlier than Kurrias. Saw you any such?"

"Nothing," said Wurrunna, "did I see but water, boodha water everywhere. But the voices of these monsters was the noise I heard, bidding the water draw me to them, and howling in rage when I got away free. I shall go swiftly to my tribe, and tell them what I have seen and heard."

Before going he gave the old wirinun some of the boodha, or salt, water, that his tribe might taste it. He also gave him a shell, one of those he had picked up on the beach.

These shells were afterward the cause of many fights,

one tribe trying to get them from the other. The oldest wirinun of the tribe always wore one of them at the great corroborees. After many generations had passed away, one wirinun, in whose possession it was, put it for safety in his Mingga, or spirit tree. And to this day there are fights about it, for he died leaving it there. Some tribes try to steal it, but others fight to protect it.

Every now and then on his road home, Wurrunna had to stop and make fresh bags to carry the salt water in, as the old ones started to leak. But at length he reached Nerangledool again, with enough for the elders of his tribe to taste.

None of them knew where he had been, nor could they imagine what this water was that stretched farther than all their hunting grounds.

Any stranger that came to the camp was brought to Wurrunna that he might hear from him what had turned him back on his journey. But what Wurrunna had seen soon became a tradition in his tribe, for he did not live long to tell his story.

He had broken the law of Baiame by leaving his own hunting ground, so was not allowed to live long after his return.

Yet so famous was he from his far journeyings that when he died a huge meteor shot across the sky, followed by a terrific crash, thereby telling the tribes for miles around that a great spirit had passed from the earth.

From generation to generation was told the story of Wurrunna's journey and the strange water he had seen, and at the big corroborees were shown the shells he had brought.

At length the Wunda, or white devils (as the Daens called the first white people), came to live in the country, and the truth of the old tradition was proved by some black boys who went down from Gundablui with cattle to Mulubinba.

There they saw the widely stretching water, with the white clouds on it. There they heard its booming roar. They were terrified, but one boy, more venturesome than the others, said, "Let us taste it. If it is salt, then in truth this is like the water the old men tell us Wurrunna saw."

They tasted it. It was salt.

"It is true," they said, "that which they told us. We will tell them that we too have seen it, and have tasted it. And we will take back some of these wa-ah to wear at the corroborees."

So back to the tribes they took the shells to prove their story.

One of those boys, the first who tasted the salt water, is an old man now. He it is who told the story of Wurrunna's trip to the sea.

The Wonders Seen by Wurrunna

WHENEVER Wurrunna the Daen was offended by anyone, he would leave his own hunting ground and travel in strange places.

One night when he was away on one of these trips it rained heavily. The next morning he saw a lot of leaves lying about.

"There are opossums here," he said, and he put his stick into a hollow tree near.

There, sure enough, he felt an opossum. He went to his fire, got some coals, which he threw down the holes in the trees to make the opossums come out. As he did so opossums from every tree around him jumped out, crying each one:

> "Naia-lerh Nuddu-waighi,
> I am a spirit opossum."

And Wurrunna saw that they were Nuddu-waighis, or spirits in the form of opossums, but having wings and long claws.

As they came out they flew toward him. Fortunately

he was a wirinun, or clever man, so had the power to change himself into his yunbeai, or familiar spirit, which was Goomble-gubbon the turkey.

In this form he flew far away from danger, then turned himself back into his own shape.

He had scarcely done so when he saw a very strange-looking man, who had no eyes and a forehead like a tomahawk. His name was Nulu-yoon-du. He used his forehead just as if it were a tomahawk, and did his chopping with it, so it saved him from carrying a tomahawk. And as he had no eyes he saw through his nose.

He gave Wurrunna a wirree, or bark holder, full of fresh honey, and seemed friendly, asking him to camp with him.

But Wurrunna did not like the look of the tomahawk forehead. Also he never could tell when Nulu-yoon-du was looking at him, so he said he was sorry but must get back to his children—whom he said he had left in the bush—but that he would return later. And off he went as fast as he could, taking the honey with him.

Next he saw a porcupine running toward him, carrying another on his back, calling as he came, "Go-oh, go-oh, go-oh," which meant, "Come, come, come."

Wurrunna looked around to see who was calling, and heard the voice coming from the porcupine, who told him he had brought his brother for Wurrunna's dinner, and he hoped he would stay and have a meal with him.

Wurrunna, who never refused food, took the porcupine, but said his children were camped a little way off and he must go and get them.

So away he went, but instead of returning, hid himself with the porcupine, and had a good meal by himself, and then a sleep with one ear open so that if the other porcupine tracked him he would hear him coming and get away.

When he was rested, off he started again. A little way off he saw Bahloo the moon shaking grubs out of a bira, or whitewood tree. Wurrunna went near and watched him, hoping to get some of the grubs for which he began to feel hungry.

After shaking the tree, Bahloo turned and pressed his back against it. Smash it went, not hurting Bahloo at all, but scattering wide of him and strewing grubs all around, which he hastened to pick up. Seeing Wurrunna's hungry look he told him to come and pick some up, too, which Wurrunna lost no time in doing. When he had as many as he could carry, he said he must go to his children and give them a meal.

"Where are they?" asked Bahloo.

"Not far," said Wurrunna.

"Then go and bring them and let them eat here—there are heaps of grubs for all."

Off hurried Wurrunna, safe away again, with another good meal provided for him. When he thought he had gone to a safe distance, he sat down and enjoyed it, very glad he had no children to share it with him.

After a rest, on he went, and next reached a country where flies and mosquitoes were more numerous and larger than he had ever seen them. He broke off a leafy twig and kept brushing them off as well as he could, but they were so bad, settling in swarms all over him in spite of his brushing, that he wondered if anyone found it possible to live in such a country.

Just as he was thinking not, he saw strange-looking objects moving ahead of him. They seemed like walking stumps sprouting with leaves, for the main part of their bodies, the trunks, were all bark-covered, while around their feet and heads were bunches of leafy twigs.

As they came nearer, Wurrunna saw they were men. Their eyes peered through holes in the bark which covered their faces. They must be so covered, he thought, to protect them from the flies and mosquitoes, but they looked so strange that they terrified Wurrunna, who cried out:

"Bulga-nunnoo! Bulga-nunnoo!
Bark-backed! Bark-backed!"

and changed himself into his familiar Goomble-gubbon and flew from that country, feeling he could not fly away quickly enough.

When he thought he must be far from it, he flew down and changed himself back to his own shape.

He next saw a number of featherless emus, and with them a man with toothless jaws, and therefore called Irra-deeboo-la.

By this time Wurrunna was really exhausted and gladly accepted the invitation of the toothless-jawed one to eat and rest with him.

But one night he was awakened from his sleep by a terrible blow across his mouth, which knocked out his front teeth. As he sprang to his feet he saw Irra-deeboo-la before him, who smilingly said, "Now you will be my brother always, being as I am, toothless, so here you will stay forever and be a companion for me."

Seeing that all around him were the featherless emus, Wurrunna agreed, but at the same time thought to himself that he would get away the first chance he had.

The next day Irra-deeboo-la told him that he and the rest were all going out hunting, and he asked Wurrunna to go too. But Wurrunna said his mouth still pained him. He would stay and try to sleep.

Off they went, and as soon as they were well out of sight Wurrunna started off in another direction and was far away before they discovered he had gone.

It was not long before he met another tribe. They were called Billoo, and were just like blackfellows, except for their feet, which were the same as an eagle-hawk's. The Billoo were kind to Wurrunna, giving him as many emu eggs as he could eat.

When he had satisfied his hunger he told them he must get back to his children.

"Where are they?" asked the Billoo.

"A little way off in the scrub," said Wurrunna.

"They must be hungry as you were," said the Billoo. "Take them some eggs, give them a meal, and then bring them here."

Wurrunna took as many eggs as he could carry, and off he went, glad so easily to make his escape, for he knew by their feet the Billoo must be too queer a tribe for him to risk staying with them.

He had seen so many strange peoples and was feeling so tired that he thought that after all he would be better off with his own tribe; but he was afraid to go back on his tracks for fear of meeting any of those he had escaped from, so he made up his mind to make a roundabout return.

Even so he met strange tribes. He came first upon the place where, long ago, he had met the Maya-mayi, or seven crystal-covered maidens, two of whom he had stolen, but who had eventually escaped from him. This they had managed by crying "Birrarl! Birrarl!" as with their stone tomahawks they struck two pine trees to which Wurrunna had sent them for bark. But the pine trees were among their relations, so at their cry had helped them to escape, rising with them clinging to the trunks until the top branches touched the sky, where the two girls found their five sisters waiting for them. And there they still are, to this day known as the Maya-mayi.

As he passed on, Wurrunna came to some clear water holes. He stooped and reached out with his hand for some water to drink. As he leaned over he saw a number of dwarfs walking about at the bottom of the hole. These dwarfs were catching fish.

They were blind, so did not see Wurrunna, but they heard him and cried out, "Where are you? Who are you?"

Wurrunna never stopped to answer, but went quickly away.

Next he saw the frog tribe, called Bun-yun Bun-yun. These frogs, at Birra-nulu's command, are said to purify all flood water.

A flood was coming when Wurrunna reached their country. When they had purified the water by throwing hot stones into it, Wurrunna saw them throw hundreds of sticks into the flood waters, which, as they touched its surface, changed into fish of all kinds.

This was the last strange tribe Wurrunna saw on his way back to his own country.

Night after night, around the campfires, he used to tell his tribe of all he had seen, and one old wirinun, or clever man, used to wag his head and say, "Na-wo. Na-wo. Yes. Yes."

And when Wurrunna had finished, the old man would tell them how, long ago, a wirinun had set out in search of the sky camping place of the greatest of all, Baiame.

This man had seen all these things and had found Baiame, who would take no notice of him, but seemed asleep with his eyes open. And when the wirinun returned he had warned his tribe never to attempt to do what he had, for all these dangers were purposely put in the way of those who were daring enough to wish to reach Baiame before their time.

Wurrunna listened, but made up his mind that what the wirinun of old had done he, too, some day, would do. What happened to him when he did is told in the legend of the black swans.

The Black Swans

WHEN Wurrunna returned to his tribe after one of his trips, he brought with him some weapons never seen by men before. These, he said, were made in a country where there were only women, and they had given them to him in exchange for his opossum-skin rug, and had said, "Go, bring us more rugs, and we will give you more weapons."

The tribes were delighted with the weapons, and agreed to go as far as the women's country with him on his next expedition to Oobi Oobi the sacred mountain, taking rugs for purpose of barter.

Wurrunna, when they started, warned his companions that there were unknown dangers on that plain, for he was sure the women were spirits. They had told him there was no death in their country, nor was there any night. The sun shone always.

He said, "When the dark rolls away from our country it does not go into theirs, which is where Yhi, our sun, being a woman, goes to rest. The dark just rolls itself under the earth until it is time to come back here. There is, too, an evil smell out on that plain, which seemed to have death in it, though the women said no death came there. We shall do well to smoke ourselves before we go out of the darkness onto that plain."

Wurrunna arranged that he would go around to the other side of the plain and make another fire to smoke them as soon as they came away, so that no evil would cling to them, and be carried back to their tribe. And in case they were staying too long, he had a plan for warning them to leave.

He would take his two brothers with him. By his magic, for he was a great wirinun, or clever man, he could turn them into two large water birds. As there were no birds on the lake, they would be quickly noticed. As soon as he had the smoke fire ready he would send his brothers swimming opposite the women's camp. Seeing them, the women would in their wonder forget the men, who were to go on to the plain and get what they wanted.

He told every man to take an animal with him, and should the women interfere, to let the animal go; there were none on the plain. The women's attention would be taken off them again; then the men must hasten to make their escape back into the darkness, where these women of the country that was always light would fear to follow them.

Each man found an animal, and then started. Among them they had opossums, native cats, flying squirrels, various kinds of rats and such.

When they reached where the darkness was rolled up on the edge of the plain, they camped. Wurrunna and his two brothers sped through the scrub, skirting the plain until they reached the far side.

Then Wurrunna lit a fire, produced a large gubbera, or crystal stone, from inside himself, and turning to his two brothers, crooned a sort of singsong over them.

Soon they cried "Biboh! Biboh!" changing as they did so into large, pure white birds.

The men on the other side of the plain, having lit their fire, were smoking themselves in it.

The women saw the smoke curling up toward their plain and ran toward it, armed with spears, crying, "Wi-bulloo! Wi-bulloo!"

One of them gave a cry of surprise, the others looked around, and there on their lake they saw swimming two huge white birds. The smoke was forgotten. They ran toward the new wonders, while the men rushed to the deserted camp for weapons.

The women saw them, and turning from the swans, came angrily toward them.

Then each man let go the animal he had. Far and wide on the plain went opossums, bandicoots, bukkandis, or native cats, and others. Shrieking after them went the women. The men dropped the opossum rugs and loaded themselves with weapons, then started toward Wurrunna's smoke signal, now curling up in a spiral column.

Having caught one of the animals, the women remembered the men, whom they saw leaving their camps laden with weapons.

Screeching with anger, they started after them, but too late. The men passed into the darkness, where they smoked all evil of the plain from them in Wurrunna's fire.

On the women came until they saw the smoke, then cried again, "Wi-bulloo! Wi-bulloo!"

They feared a fire as much as they feared the dark, both unknown in their country.

Failing to get their weapons, they turned again to where the strange white birds had been. But they had gone.

The women were so angry that they began to quarrel, and from words they got to blows. Their blood flowed fast, and freely stained the whole of the western sky, where their country is. Ever since, when the tribes see a red sunset they say, "Look at the blood of the Wi-bulloos, they must be fighting again."

The men returned to their own country with their weapons, and Wurrunna traveled on alone toward the sacred mountain, which was to the northeast of Wi-bulloo land.

He forgot all about his brothers, though they flew after him, crying, "Biboh! Biboh!" to attract his attention, that he might change them back to men.

But heedlessly on went Wurrunna, up the stone steps cut in the sacred mountain for the coming of Baiame to earth.

The swans, tired of flying, stayed on a small lagoon at the foot of the mountain. As the eagle-hawks, the messengers of the spirits, were flying to deliver a spirit's message, they saw in their own lagoon two strange white birds.

In their rage they swooped down, drove their huge claws and sharp beaks into the poor white swans.

They then clutched them up with their claws, and flew far away from the sacred mountain, over plains and over mountain ranges, away to the south.

Every now and then, in savage rage, they stopped to pluck out a handful of feathers, white as the ash of gidya wood. These feathers fluttered down the sides of the mountains, lodging in between the rocks, blood dripping beside them.

On flew the eagle-hawks, until they came to a large lagoon near to the big salt water. At one end of the lagoon were rocks. On these they dropped the swans, then swooped down themselves, and savagely started to pluck out the few feathers the birds had left. But just as they were tearing out the last on the wings, they recollected that they

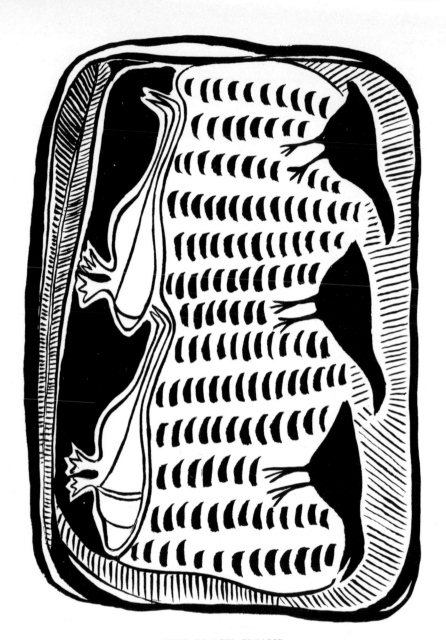

THE BLACK SWANS

This is just the end part of the story where the mountain crows drop their feathers on the poor wounded, featherless Baiamul brothers, turning them into the black swans.

had not delivered the message of the spirits, so, fearing their anger, the eagle-hawks left the swans and flew back to their own country.

The poor Baiamul brothers crouched together, almost featherless, bleeding, cold and miserable. They felt they were dying, far away from their tribe.

Suddenly, softly fell on them a shower of feathers, which covered their shivering bodies. Gaining warmth, they looked about them. High on the trees overhead they saw hundreds of mountain crows, such as they had sometimes seen in the plains country, and had believed to be a warning of evil.

The crows called to them, "The eagle-hawks are our enemies, too. We saw you left by them to die. We said it should not be so. On the breeze we sent some of our feathers to warm you, and make you strong to fly back to your friends, and laugh at the eagle-hawks."

The black feathers covered the swans all but on their wings, where a few white ones had been left. Also the down under the black feathers was white down. The red blood on their beaks stayed there forever.

The white swan feathers that the eagle-hawks had plucked out when crossing the mountains took root where they fell, and sprang up as the soft white flowers which you call flannel flowers.

Baiamul, the swans, flew back over the camp of their tribe. Wurrunna heard their cry, "Biboh! Biboh!" and knew it was the voice of his brothers, though when he looked up he saw not white birds, but black, with red bills.

Sorrowful as he was at their sad cry, Wurrunna had no power to change them back to men. His power as a wirinun had been taken from him for daring to go, before his time, to Baiame's sky camp.

Where the Frost Comes From

THE Maya-mayi once lived on this earth. They were seven sisters remarkable for their beauty. They had long hair to their waists, and their bodies sparkled with icicles.

Their father and mother lived among the rocks away on some distant mountain, staying there always, never wandering about as their daughters did. When the sisters used to go hunting they never joined any other tribes, though many tried from time to time to make friends with them. One large family of boys in particular thought them so beautiful that they wished them to stay with them and be their wives. These boys, the Berai Berai, used to follow the Maya-mayi about, and watching where they camped, used to leave there offerings for them.

The Berai Berai had great skill in finding the nests of bees. First they would catch a bee, and stick some white down or a white feather with some gum on its back between

174

its hind legs. Then they would let it go, and follow it to its nest. The honey they found they would put in wirrees, or bark vessels, which they left at the camps of the Maya-mayi, who ate the honey, but listened not to the wooing.

But one day, as you know, old Wurrunna stole two of the girls, capturing them by stratagem. He tried to warm the icicles off them, but succeeded only in putting out his fire.

After a time of captivity the two stolen girls were lifted to the sky. There they found their five sisters stationed. With them they have since remained, not shining quite so brightly as the other five, having been dulled by the warmth of Wurrunna's fires.

When the Berai Berai found that the Maya-mayi had left this earth forever, they were inconsolable. Maidens of their own tribe were offered to them, but as they could not have the Maya-mayi they would have none. Refusing to be comforted they would not eat, and so pined away and died. The spirits were sorry for them, and pleased with their faithfulness, so they gave them, too, a place in the sky. And there they are still.

(Orion's sword and belt we call them, but to the Daens they are still known as Berai Berai, the boys.)

The Daens say the Berai Berai still hunt the bees by day, and at night dance corroborees, which the Maya-mayi sing for them. For though the Maya-mayi stay in their own camp at some distance form the Berai Berai, they are not too far away for their songs to be heard. The Daens say, too, that the Maya-mayi will shine forever as an example to all women on earth.

At one time of the year, in remembrance that they once lived on earth, the Maya-mayi break off some ice from themselves and throw it down. When, on waking in the morning, the Daens see ice everywhere, they say, "The

Maya-mayi have not forgotten us. They have thrown some of their ice down. We will show we remember them too."

Then they take a piece of ice, and hold it to the septum of the noses of those children who have not already had theirs pierced. When the septums are numb with the cold, they are pierced, and a straw or bone placed through them. "Now," say the Daens; "these children will be able to sing as the Maya-mayi sing."

A relation of the Maya-mayi was looking down at the earth when the two sisters were being lifted to the sky. When he saw how the old man from whom they had escaped ran about blustering and ordering them down again, he was so amused at Wurrunna's defeat, and glad at their escape, that he burst out laughing, and has been laughing ever since, being still known as the Laughing Star to the Daens.

When thunder is heard in the wintertime, the Daens say, "There are the Maya-mayi bathing again. That is the noise they make as they jump, doubled up, into the water, when playing Buba-larmay, for whoever makes the loudest flop wins the game, which is a favorite one with the earth people too."

When the noise of the Buba-larmay of the Maya-mayi is heard the Daens say, too, "Soon rain will fall, the Maya-mayi will splash the water down. It will reach us in three days."

The Dancing Bird

B ROLGA NUM-BA-DI was very fond of
going out hunting with her young daughter Brolga. Her
tribe used to tell her she was foolish to do so, that some
day the Wurra-wilberoo would catch them.

It was not for old Brolga Num-ba-di that the Daens
cared, but all the camp were proud of young Brolga. She
was the merriest girl and the best dancer of all her tribe,
the women of whom were for the most part content to click
the boomerangs, beat their rolled-up opossum-skin rugs,
and sing the corroboree songs in voices from shrill to sweet
while the men danced; but not so Brolga. She must dance,
too; and not only the dances she saw the rest dance, but
new ones which she taught herself, for every song she heard
she set to steps. Sometimes, with laughing eyes, she would
whirl around like a boolee, or whirlwind. Then suddenly
she would change to a stately measure, then for variety's
sake perform a series of swift twirlings, as if, indeed, a whirlwind had her in his grip.

The fame of her dancing spread abroad, and proud in-

deed was the tribe to whom she belonged; hence their anxiety for her safety, and their dread that the Wurra-wilberoo would catch her.

The Wurra-wilberoo were two cannibals who lived in the scrub alone.

But in spite of all warnings, Brolga Num-ba-di continued to hunt as usual with only her daughter for companion.

One day they went out to camp for two or three days. Nothing hurt them the first night, but the next day the Wurra-wilberoo surprised and captured them. They gave Brolga Num-ba-di a severe blow. She fell down and feigned death, lest they should strike her again and kill her. The

Wurra-wilberoo picked her up to carry her off to their camp. They did not wish to hurt young Brolga; they meant to keep her to dance for them. They told her so, and gave her their muggil, or stone knife, to carry, telling her to fear nothing and come with them.

She went with them, but when they were not looking she threw the knife away.

As soon as they reached the camp, the Wurra-wilberoo asked her for it. They wanted to cut up Brolga Num-ba-di before cooking her. Brolga said she put the muggil down where they had rested, some way back, and had forgotten it.

They said, "We will go back and get it. You stay here."

They started. When they were some way off, the mother said, "Are they out of sight yet?"

"Not yet. Wait a little while."

Brolga watched them go right away, then told her mother, who immediatel. jumped up. Then off went both mother and daughter as fast as they could to their own tribe, to tell what had happened.

When the Wurra-wilberoo came back to their camp, they were enraged to find not only the daughter but the mother gone, even she whom they had left, as they thought, dead. No feast, no dance for them that night unless they recovered their victims, whose tracks showed that Brolga had actually been able to run beside her daughter.

"She only pretended to be dead," they said, "to deceive us. We will hasten and overtake them before they reach the tribe. Yes, even if they are with the tribe we will snatch them away."

But the Daens were looking out for them, fully armed. Seeing this the Wurra-wilberoo turned and fled, the Daens after them in quick pursuit. But they failed to overtake them, and fearing to follow them too far lest a trap lay ready for them, the Daens returned to their camp. But so angry were they at the attempt to capture their precious Brolga that a council was held, and the destruction of the Wurra-wilberoo determined upon.

Two of the cleverest wirinuns said they would send their Mullee Mullees, or dream spirits, in whirlwinds after the enemy to catch them.

This they did. Whirling along went the boolees with the Mullee Mullees in them. Quickly they went along the track of the Wurra-wilberoo, whom they soon overtook, turning them back toward the camp whence they had fled.

"We will go," said one of the Wurra-wilberoo to the other, "back to the camp, ahead of these whirlwinds. We will seize the girl and her mother and fly in another direction. The whirlwinds will miss us in the camp and seize others. We will not be balked. Young Brolga shall be ours to dance before us, and her mother shall make our supper tonight."

On, on they fled before the whirlwinds, which gained both size and pace as they followed them.

The Daens were so astonished at seeing the Wurra-wilberoo returning straight toward them, the whirlwinds after them, that they never thought of arming themselves. In the midst of them rushed the Wurra-wilberoo. One seized Brolga Num-ba-di, the other young Brolga, and before the astonished Daens realized their coming, the Wurra-wilberoo had gone some distance along the edge of the plain.

"Bring your weapons," roared the Mullee Mullees in the whirlwinds to the Daens as they swirled through the camp after the enemy.

The Wurra-wilberoo carrying young Brolga was ahead. The other, finding the whirlwinds were gaining on them, dropped his burden, Brolga Num-ba-di, and ran on. Just in front of them were two huge belah trees. Feeling that the whirlwinds, which they now knew must have spirits in them, were already lifting them off their feet, the Wurra-wilberoo clung to the belah trees. The one who had captured young Brolga still held her with one arm while he grasped the tree with the other.

"Let the girl go," shouted the other to him. "Save yourself."

"They shall never have her," he answered savagely. "If I have to lose her they shall not get her."

Then as the whirlwinds howled around them, tearing up everything in a wild fury, the belah trees now in their grasp creaking and groaning, the Wurra-wilberoo muttered a sort of incantation and released young Brolga. As she slipped from his grasp a shout of joy came from the Daens, who were just in the wake of the whirlwinds. They had their spears poised, but had been frightened to throw for fear of injuring Brolga.

But their hope of vengeance was short-lived. The whirlwinds wound around the belah trees to which the Wurra-wilberoo clung, and dragged them from the roots before the men could let go. Up, up the whirlwinds carried the trees, the Wurra-wilberoo still clinging to them, until they reached the sky. There they planted them not far from the Milky Way.

(And there they are still, two dark spots, called Wurra-wilberoo, for the two cannibals have lived in them ever since. They are dreaded by all who have to pass along the Warrambool, or Milky Way, where are camped many old Daens. They cook the grubs they have gathered for food, and the smoke of their fires shows the course of the Warrambool. But no one can reach these fires unless the Wurra-wilberoo are away, as sometimes happens when they go down to the earth and, taking the shape of boolees, pursue their old enemies the Daens.)

When the Daens saw their enemies were gone, they

turned to get Brolga. Her mother was already with them.

But where was young Brolga? She had not been seen to move away, yet she was gone.

All around the plain they looked. They saw only a tall bird walking across it. They went to the place whence the trees had been wrenched. They searched the ground for tracks, but saw none of Brolga's going away, only those of the big cranelike bird now on the plain. Wurra-wilberoo must have seized her again and taken her after all, they said.

As soon as the Mullee Mullees, which had been in the whirlwinds, returned from placing the belah trees and the Wurra-wilberoo in the sky, the wirinuns asked them if they had left her there.

No, they said, Brolga had not gone to the sky. Surely the Daens had seen the Wurra-wilberoo let her go?

Then where was she?

That no one could say, and no one thought of asking the big bird on the plain.

All mourned for Brolga as for one dead. Her spirit, they said, would haunt the camp because they could not find her body to bury it, though they knew she must be dead; otherwise would she not return to them?

They moved their camp away to the other side of the plain.

After a while they noticed that a number of birds, like the one they had seen on the plain at the time of Brolga's disappearance, came feeding around not far from their camp, and that after feeding for a while these birds would begin to corroboree, such a strange corroboree, of which one bird taller than the others was seemingly a leader. This corroboree dance was so human, like no movements of any other birds, indeed like nothing of the sort that the Daens had ever before seen, unless it were the dances of the lost Brolga.

Out onto a clear space the leader would lead her troupe. There would be much craning of necks, and bowing, pirouetting, stately measured changing of places; then twirling with wings extended, just as Brolga used to fling out her arms before she whirled madly round and round, as these birds did now. Seeing this likeness the Daens called, "Brolga! Brolga!"

The bird seemed to understand, for it looked toward them, then led its troupe into wilder and more intricate figures of the corroboree.

As time went on, the leader of the birds was seen no more, but so well had her troupe learned the corroborees that they went through the same grotesque performances as in her time.

The old Daens who remembered the dancing girl Brolga died, but all these dancing birds were known forever by her name.

When Brolga Num-ba-di died she was taken to the sky, there to live forever with her daughter Brolga. (Both known to us as the Magellanic Clouds, to the Daens as the Brolga.)

There Brolga Num-ba-di learned that the Wurra-wilberoo by his incantation had changed her daughter into the dancing bird, a shape she had to keep as long as she lived on earth.

Afterward, if ever the Daens saw a boolee speeding along near their camp, the women would cry, "Wurra-wilberoo," clutch their children and bury their heads in their rugs; the men would seize their weapons and hurl them at the ever-feared and hated capturers of Brolga.

The Wi-oombeens and Piggi-billa

Two Wi-oombeen brothers went out hunt-
ing. One brother was much younger and smaller than the
other, so when they sighted an emu the elder one said to
the younger, "You stay quietly here and do not make a
noise, or Piggi-billa, whose camp we passed just now, will
hear you and steal the emu if I kill it. He is so strong.
I'll go on and try to kill the emu with this stone."

The little Wi-oombeen watched his big brother sneak
up to the emu, crawling along, almost flat on the ground.
He saw him get quite close to the emu, then spring up
quickly and throw the stone with such accurate aim as
to kill the bird on the spot. The little brother was so re-
joiced that he forgot his brother's caution, and he called
aloud in his joy. The big Wi-oombeen looked around and
gave him a warning sign, but too late. Piggi-billa had
heard the cry and was hastening toward them. Quickly
big Wi-oombeen left the emu and joined his little brother.

When he came up Piggi-billa said, "What have you
found?"

"Nothing," said the big Wi-oombeen, "nothing but
some mistletoe berries."

"It must have been something more than that, or your little brother would not have called out so loudly."

Little Wi-oombeen was so afraid that Piggi-billa would find their emu and take it that he said, "I hit a little bird with a stone, and I was glad I could throw so straight."

"It was no cry for the killing of a little bird or for the finding of mistletoe berries that I heard. It was for something much more than either, or you would not have called out so joyfully. If you do not tell me at once, I will kill you both."

The Wi-oombeen brothers were frightened, for Piggi-billa was a great fighter and very strong, so when they saw he was really angry they showed him the dead emu.

"Just what I want for my supper," he said, and so saying dragged it away to his own camp.

The Wi-oombeens followed him and even helped him to make a fire to cook the emu, hoping by so doing to get a share given to them. But Piggi-billa would not give them any. He said he must have it all for himself.

Angry and disappointed, the Wi-oombeens marched straight off and told some blackfellows who lived near that Piggi-billa had a fine fat emu just cooked for supper.

Up jumped the blackfellows, seized their spears, bade the Wi-oombeens quickly lead them to Piggi-billa's camp, promising them, for so doing, a share of the emu.

When they were within range of spearshot, the blackfellows formed a circle, took aim and threw their spears at Piggi-billa.

As the spears fell thick on him, sticking out all over him, Piggi-billa cried aloud, "Bingge-la, Bingge-la. You can have it. You can have it."

But the blackfellows did not desist until Piggi-billa was too wounded even to cry out. Then they left him a mass of spears and turned to look for the emu. But to their surprise they found it not. Then for the first time they missed the Wi-oombeens.

Looking around they saw their tracks going to where the emu had evidently been. Then they saw that they had dragged the emu to their nunnoo, or humpy made of grass.

When the Wi-oombeens saw the blackfellows coming they caught hold of the emu and dragged it to a big hole they knew of, with a big stone at its entrance, which only they knew the secret of moving. They moved the stone, got the emu and themselves into the hole, and the stone in place again before the blackfellows reached the place.

The blackfellows tried to move the stone, but could not. Yet they knew that the Wi-oombeens must have done so, for they had tracked them right up to it, and they could hear the sound of their voices on the other side of it. They saw there was a crevice on either side of the stone, between it and the ground. Through these crevices they drove in their spears, thinking they must surely kill the brothers. But the Wi-oombeens too had seen these crevices and had expected the spears, so that they had placed the dead emu before them to act as a shield. And into its body were driven the spears of the blackfellows intended for the Wi-oombeens.

Having driven the spears well in, the blackfellows went off to get help to move the stone, but when they had gone a little way they heard the Wi-oombeens laughing. Back they came and speared again, and again started for help, as they left only to hear once more the laughter of the brothers.

The Wi-oombeens, finding their laughter only brought back the blackfellows to a fresh attack, determined to keep quiet, which, after the next spearing, they did.

Quite sure, when they heard their spearshots followed

by neither conversation nor laughter, that they had killed the Wi-oombeens at last, the blackfellows hurried away to bring back the full strength and cunning of the camp, to remove the stone.

The Wi-oombeens hurriedly discussed what plan they had better adopt to elude the blackfellows, for well they knew that should they ever meet any of them again they would be killed without mercy. And as they talked they satisfied their hunger by eating some of the emu flesh.

After a while the blackfellows returned, and soon was the stone removed from the entrance. Some of them crept into the hole, where, to their surprise, they found only the remains of the emu and no trace of the Wi-oombeens. As those who had gone in first, crept out and told of the disappearance of the Wi-oombeens, others, not believing such a story, crept in to find it was so.

They searched around for tracks. Seeing that their spears were all in the emu it seemed to them probable that the Wi-oombeens had escaped alive, and if so, their tracks would show whither they had gone. But search as they would no tracks could the blackfellows find. All they could see were two little birds that sat on a bush near the hole, watching them all the time.

The little birds flew around the hole sometimes, but never away, always returning to their bush and seeming to be discussing the whole affair. But what they said the blackfellows could not understand.

But as time went on and no sign was ever found of the Wi-oombeens, the blackfellows became sure that the brothers had turned into the little white-throated birds that had sat on the bush by the hole, in order, they supposed, to escape their vengeance.

And ever afterward the little white-throats were called

Wi-oombeens. And the memory of Piggi-billa is perpetu-
ated by a porcupine anteater, which bears his name, and
whose skin is closely covered with miniature spears sticking
out all over it.

Piggi-billa the Porcupine

PIGGI-BILLA was getting old and not able to do much hunting for himself. Nor did he care so much for the flesh of emu and kangaroo as he did for the flesh of men.

He used to entice young men to his camp by various devices, and then kill and eat them.

At last the Daens found out what he was doing. They were very angry, and determined to punish him.

"We will kill or cripple him," they said, "so that he, giant though he be, shall be powerless against our people."

A mob of them went and surrounded his camp.

He was lying asleep, face downward, as he did not wish his Doowi, or dream spirit, to leave him, as it might have done had he slept on his back, with his mouth open.

In his sleep even he seemed to hear a rustling in the leaves, but suspected no evil, saying drowsily to himself, "It is but the Bulla Bulla, or butterflies, fluttering around."

Then he slept on while his enemies closed in around him.

Raising their spears, with one accord they threw them

189

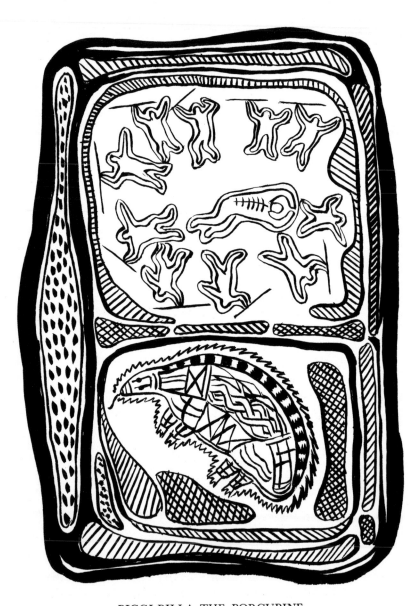

PIGGI-BILLA THE PORCUPINE

Piggi-billa lies asleep face down and the Daens gather around to spear him. The other part of the picture is after he has crawled away full of the spears that have remained in his back ever since.

at him, until his back was one mass of them sticking up all over it. Then the Daens rushed in, and broke his arms and legs, with their boondis and woggaras, or wooden battle axes, crippling him indeed. As he made neither sound nor movement, they thought they had killed him, and satisfied with their vengeance, went back to the camp, meaning to return for their weapons later.

As soon as the Daens were gone, Piggi-billa crawled away on all fours to the underground home of his friend Murga Muggai the spider. Down he went through the trap door, and there he stayed until his wounds were healed.

He tried to draw out the spears, but was unable to do so. They stayed in his back forever, and forever he went on all fours, as his tribe has done ever since. They, too, as he did, go quickly underground if in danger from enemies.

Beereeun the Miragemaker

BEEREEUN the lizard wanted to marry
Bullai Bullai the green parrot sisters. But they did not
want to marry him. They liked Weedah the mockingbird
better. Their mother said they must marry Beereeun, for
she had pledged them to him at their births, and Beereeun
was a great wirinun and would harm them if they did
not keep her pledge.

When Weedah came back from hunting they told him
what their mother had said, how they had been pledged
to Beereeun, who now claimed them.

"Tomorrow," said Weedah, "old Beereeun goes to meet
a tribe coming from the Springs country. While he is away
we will go toward the Big River, and burn the track behind us. I will go out as if to hunt as usual in the morning.
I will hide myself in the thick gidya scrub. You two must
follow later and meet me there. We will then cross the
big plain where the grass is now thick and dry. Bring with
you a fire stick. We will throw it back into the plain, then
no one can follow our tracks. On we will go to the Big
River. There I have a friend who has a goombeelga, a

bark canoe. Then shall we be safe from pursuit, for he will put us over the river. And we can travel on and on even to the country of the short-armed people if so we choose."

The next morning ere Goo-goor-gaga had ceased his laughter Weedah had started.

Some hours later, in the gidya scrub, the Bullai Bullai sisters joined him.

Having crossed the big plain they threw back a fire stick where the grass was thick and dry. The fire spread quickly through it, crackling and throwing up tongues of flame.

Through another scrub went the three, then across another plain, through another scrub and onto a plain again.

The day was hot, Yhi the sun was high in the sky. They became thirsty, but saw no water, and had brought none in their haste.

"We want water," the Bullai Bullai cried.

"Why did you not bring some?" said Weedah.

"We thought you had plenty, or would travel as the creeks run, or at least know of a goola-gool, a water-holding tree."

"We shall soon reach water. Look even now ahead, there is water."

The Bullai Bullai looked eagerly toward where he pointed, and there in truth, on the far side of the plain, they saw a sheet of water. They quickened their steps, but the farther they went, the farther off seemed the water, but on they went ever hoping to reach it. Across the plain they went, only to find that on the other side of a belt of timber the water had gone.

The weary girls would have lain down, but Weedah said that they would surely reach water on the other side of the wood. Again they struggled on through the scrub to another plain.

"There it is! I told you so! There is the water."

And looking ahead they again saw a sheet of water.

Again their hopes were raised, and though the sun beat fiercely, on they marched, only to be again disappointed.

"Let us go back," they said. "This is the country of evil spirits. We see water, and when we come where we have seen it there is but dry earth. Let us go back."

"Back to Beereeun, who would kill you?"

"Better to die from the blow of a boondi in your own country than of thirst in a land of devils. We will go back."

"Not so. Not with a boondi would he kill you, but with a gooweera, a poison stick. Slow would be your death, and you would be always in pain until your shadow was wasted away. But why talk of returning? Did we not set fire to the big plain? Could you cross that? Waste not your breath, but follow me. See, there again is water!"

But the Bullai Bullai had lost hope. No longer would they even look up, though time after time Weedah called out, "Water ahead of us! Water ahead of us!" only to disappoint them again and again.

At last the Bullai Bullai became so angry with him that they seized him and beat him. But even as they beat him he cried all the time, "Water is there! Water is there!"

Then he implored them to let him go, and he would drag up the roots from some water trees and drain the water from them.

"Yonder I see a coolabah. From its roots I can drain enough to quench your thirst. Or here beside us is a bingawingul; full of water are its roots. Let me go. I will drain them for you."

But the Bullai Bullai had no faith in his promises, and they but beat him the harder until they were exhausted.

When they ceased to beat him and let him go, Weedah went on a little way, then lay down, feeling bruised all over, and thankful that the night had come and the fierce sun no longer scorched them.

One Bullai Bullai said to her sister, "Could we not sing the song our Bargi used to sing, and make the rain fall?"

"Let us try, if we can make a sound with our dry throats," said the other.

"We will sing to our cousin Dooloomai the thunder. He will hear us, and break a rain cloud for us."

So they sat down, rocking their bodies to and fro, and beating their knees, sang:

> "Moogaray, Moogaray, May, May,
> Eehu, Eehu, Doon-gara."

> "Hailstones, hailstones, wind, wind,
> Rain, rain, lightning."

Over and over again they sang these words as they had heard their Bargi, or mother's mother, do. Then for themselves they added:

> "Eehu oonah wambaneah Dooloomai
> Bullul goonung inderh gingnee
> Eehu oonah wambaneah Dooloomai."

> "Give us rain, Thunder, our cousin,
> Thirsting for water are we,
> Give us rain, Thunder, our cousin."

As long as their poor parched throats could make a sound they sang this. Then they lay down to die, weary and hopeless. One said faintly, "The rain will be too late, but surely it is coming, for strong is the smell of the gidya."

"Strong indeed," said the other.

But even this sure sign to their tribe that rain is near roused them not. It would come, they thought, too late for them. But even then away in the north a thunder-

cloud was gathering. It rolled across the sky quickly, peal-
ing out thunder calls as it came to tell of its coming. It
stopped right over the plain in front of the Bullai Bullai.
One more peal of thunder, which opened the cloud, then
splashing down came the first big drops of rain. Slowly
and few they came until just at the last, when a quick,
heavy shower fell, emptying the thundercloud, and filling
the gilguy holes on the plain.

The cool splashing of the rain on their hot, tired limbs
gave new life to the Bullai Bullai and to Weedah. They
all ran to the gilguy holes. Stooping their heads, they drank
and quenched their thirst.

"I told you the water was here," said Weedah. "You
see I was right."

"No water was here when you said so. If our cousin
Dooloomai had not heard our song for his help, we should
have died, and you too."

And they were angry. But Weedah dug them some
roots, and when they ate they forgot their anger. When
their meal was over they lay down to sleep.

The next morning on they went again. That day they
again again saw across the plains the same strange semblance of water that had lured them on before. They knew
not what it could be, they knew only that it was not
water.

Just at dusk they came to the Big River. There they
saw Goolay-yali the pelican, with his canoe. Weedah asked
him to put them over onto the other side. He said he
would do so one at a time, as the canoe was small. First
he said he would take Weedah, that he might get ready
a camp of the long grass in the bend of the river. He took
Weedah over. Then back he came and, fastening his canoe,
he went up to the Bullai Bullai, who were sitting beside
the remains of his old fire.

"Now," said Goolay-yali, "you two will go with me to

my camp, which is down in that bend. Weedah cannot get over again. You shall live with me. I shall catch fish to feed you. I have some even now in my camp cooking. There, too, have I wirrees of honey, and durri ready for the baking. Weedah has nothing to give you but the grass nunnoos he is but now making."

"Take us to Weedah," they said.

"Not so," said Goolay-yali, and he stepped forward as if to seize them.

The Bullai Bullai stooped and filled their hands with the white ashes of the burned-out fire, which they flung at him.

Handful after handful they threw at him until he stood before them white, all but his hands, which he spread out and shook, thus freeing them from the cloud of ashes enveloping him and obscuring his sight.

Having thus checked him, the Bullai Bullai ran to the bank of the river, meaning to get the canoe and cross over to Weedah.

But in the canoe, to their horror, was Beereeun! Beereeun, whom to escape they had sped across plain and through scrub.

Yet here he was, while between them and Weedah lay the wide river.

They had not known it, but Beereeun had been near them all the while. He it was who had made the mirage on each plain, thinking he would lure them on by this semblance of water until they perished of thirst. From that fate Dooloomai, their cousin the thunder, had saved them. But now the chance of Beereeun had come.

The Bullai Bullai looked across the wide river and saw the nunnoos, or grass shelters, Weedah had made. They saw him running in and out of them as if he were playing a game, not thinking of them at all. Strange nunnoos they were too, having both ends open.

Seeing where they were looking, Beereeun said, "Weedah is womba, deaf. I stole his Doowi while he slept and put in its place a mad spirit. He knows naught of you now. He cares naught for you. It is so with those who look too long at the mirage. He will trouble me no more, nor you. Why look at him?"

But the Bullai Bullai could not take their eyes from Weedah, so strangely he went on, unceasingly running in at one end of the grass nunnoo, through it and out of the other.

"He is womba," they said, but yet they could not understand it. They looked toward him and called him, though he heeded them not.

"I will send him far from you," said Beereeun, getting angry. He seized a spear, stood up in the canoe and sent it swiftly through the air into Weedah, who gave a great cry, screamed "Water is there! Water is there!" and fell back dead.

"Take us over! Take us over!" cried the Bullai Bullai. "We must go to him, we might yet save him."

"He is all right. He is in the sky. He is not there," said Beereeun. "If you want him you must follow him to the sky. Look, you can see him there now." And he pointed to a star that the Bullai Bullai had never seen before.

"There he is, Womba."

Across to the grass nunnoo the Bullai Bullai looked, but no Weedah was there. Then they sat down and wailed a death song, for they knew well they should see Weedah no more. They plastered their heads with white ashes and water; they tied on their bodies green twigs; then, cutting themselves till the blood ran, they lit some smoke branches and smoked themselves, as widows.

Beereeun spoke to Goolay-yali the pelican, saying, "There is no brother of the dead man to marry these women. In this country they have no relation. You shall take one, and I the other. Tonight when they sleep we will each seize one."

"That which you say shall be," said Goolay-yali the pelican.

But the sisters heard what they said, though they gave no sign and mourned the dead Weedah without ceasing. And with their death song they mingled a cry to all of their tribe who were dead to help them, and save them from these men who would seize them while they were still mourning, before they had swallowed the smoke water, or their tribe had heard the voice of their dead.

As the night wore on, the wailing of the women ceased. The men thought that they were at length asleep, and crept up to their camp. But it was empty! Gone were the Bullai Bullai!

The men heaped fuel on their fire to light up the darkness, but yet saw no sign of the Bullai Bullai.

They heard a sound, a sound of mocking laughter. They looked around, but saw nothing.

Again they heard a sound of laughter. Whence came it? Again it echoed through the air.

It was from the sky. They looked up. It was the new star Womba, mocking them. Womba who once was Weedah, who laughed aloud to see that the Bullai Bullai had escaped their enemies, for even now they were stealing along the sky toward him, which the men on earth saw.

"We have lost them," said Beereeun. "I shall make a roadway to the skies and follow them. Thence shall I bring them back, or wreak my vengeance on them."

He went to the canoe where were his spears. Having grasped them, he took, too, the spears of Goolay-yali, which lay by the smoldering fire.

He chose a barbed one. With all his force he threw it

up to the sky. The barb caught there, the spear hung down. Beereeun threw another, which caught on to the first, and yet another, and so on, each catching the one before it, until he could touch the lowest from the earth. This he clutched hold of, and climbed up, up, up, until he reached the sky. Then he started in pursuit of the Bullai Bullai. And he is still pursuing them.

Since then the tribe of Beereeun have always been able to swarm up sheer heights. Since then, too, his tribe, the little lizards of the plains, make eer-dher, or mirages, to lure on thirsty travelers, only to send them mad before they die of thirst. Since then Goolay-yali the pelican has been white, for ever did the ashes thrown by the Bullai Bullai cling to him; only where he had shaken them off from his hands are there a few black feathers. The tribe of Bullai Bullai are colored like the green of the leaves the sisters strung on themselves in which to mourn Weedah, with here and there a dash of whitish yellow and red, caused by the ashes and the blood of their mourning. And Womba the star, the mad star, still shines (our Canopus). And Weedah the mockingbird still builds grass nunnoos, open at both ends, in and out of which he runs, as if they were but playgrounds.

And the fire which Weedah and the Bullai Bullai made spread from one end of the country to the other, over ridges and across plains, burning the trees so that their trunks have been black ever since. Deenyi, the iron barks, smoldered the longest of all, and their trunks were so seared that the seams are deeply marked in their thick black bark still, making them show out grimly distinct on the ridges, to remind the Daens forever of Beereeun the miragemaker.

Gooloo the Magpie and the Waroogas

G o o l o o the magpie was a very old woman, and a very wicked old woman too, as this story will tell.

During all the past season, when the grass was thick with seed, she had gathered much doonbur, or seed, which she crushed into meal as she wanted it for food. She used to crush it on a big flat stone with small flat stones—the big stone was called a dayoorl. Gooloo ground a great deal of the doonbur seed to put away for immediate use. The rest she kept whole, to be ground up as required.

Soon after she had finished her first grinding, a neighboring tribe came along and camped near where she was.

One day the men all went out hunting, leaving the women and the children in the camp. After the men had been gone a little while, Gooloo the magpie came to their camp to talk to the women.

"Why do you not go hunting too?" she said. "Many are the nests of warra-nunnas around here, and thick is the honey in them. Many and ripe are the bumbels hanging now on the bumbel trees. Red is the fruit of the gruees, and opening with ripeness is the fruit of the gweebets.

Yet you sit in the camp and hunger until your husbands return with the dinewan and bohra they have gone forth to slay. Go, women, and gather of the plenty that surrounds you. I will take care of your children, the little waroogas."

"Your words are wise," the women said. "It is foolish to sit here and hunger, when near at hand yams are thick in the ground, and many fruits wait but the plucking. We will go and fill quickly our kumbis and goolays, but our children we will take with us."

"Not so," said Gooloo. "Foolish indeed were you to do that. You would tire the little feet of those that run, and tire yourselves with the burden of those that have to be carried. No, take forth your kumbis and goolays empty, that you may bring back the more. Many are the spoils that wait only the hand of the gatherer. Look ye, I have a durri made of fresh doonbur seed, cooking just now on that bark between two fires; that shall your children eat, and swiftly shall I make them another. They shall eat and be full ere their mothers are out of sight. See, they come to me now, they are hungry for durri, and well will I feed them. Haste you then, that you may return in time to make ready the fires for cooking the meat your husbands will bring. Glad will your husbands be when they see you have filled your goolays and kumbis with fruits, and your wirrees with honey. Haste you, I say, and do well."

Having listened to the words of Gooloo, the women decided to do as she said. Leaving their children with her, they started forth with empty kumbis and armed with kumbus, with which to chop out the bees' nests and opossums, and with yam sticks to dig up yams.

When the women had gone Gooloo gathered the children around her and fed them with durri, hot from the coals. Honey, too, she gave them, and bumbels, or wild oranges, which she had buried to ripen.

When they had eaten she hurried them off to her real home, built in a hollow tree, a little distance away from where she had been cooking her durri. Into her tree she hurriedly thrust them, followed quickly herself, and made all secure.

Here she fed them again, but the children had already satisfied their hunger, and now they missed their mothers and began to cry. Their crying reached the ears of the women as they were returning to their camp. Quickly they came at that sound, which is not good in a mother's ears. As they quickened their steps they thought how soon the spoils that lay heavy in their kumbis would comfort their children.

Soon they reached the camp, but, alas! where were their children? And where was Gooloo the magpie?

"They are playing wahgoo," they said, "and have hidden themselves."

The mothers hunted all around for them, and called aloud the names of their children and of Gooloo. But no answer could they hear and no trace could they find. And yet every now and then they heard the sound of children wailing.

Then loudly wailed the mothers themselves for their lost waroogas, and wailing, returned to the camp to wait the coming of the blackfellows.

Heavy were their hearts, and sad were their faces when their husbands returned. They hastened to tell the black-fellows when they came how Gooloo had persuaded them to go hunting, promising if they did so that she would feed the hungry waroogas, and care for them while they were away, but—and here they wailed again for their poor waroogas.

Then they told how they had listened to Gooloo's words and gone. Truth had she told of the plenty around; their kumbis and goolays were full of fruits and spoils they had gathered, but, alas, they had come home with them laden only to find their children gone and Gooloo gone too. And no trace could they find of either, though at times they heard a sound as of children wailing.

Then angry were the men, saying, "What mothers are you to leave your young to a stranger, and that stranger a Gooloo, ever a treacherous race? Did we not go forth to gain food for you and our children? Saw you ever your husbands return from the chase empty-handed? Then why, when you knew we were gone hunting, must you too go forth and leave our helpless ones to a stranger? Oh, evil, evil indeed is the time that has come when a mother forgets her child! Stay you in the camp while we go forth to hunt for our lost waroogas. Heavy will be our hands on the women if we return without them!"

The men hunted the bush around for miles, but found no trace of the lost waroogas, though they, too, heard at times a noise as of children's voices wailing.

But beyond the wailing, which echoed in the mothers' ears forever, no trace was ever found of the children. For many days the women sat in the camp mourning for their lost waroogas, and beating their heads because they had listened to the voice of Gooloo the magpie.

The Black-breasted Magpie

ONE afternoon Moogra-ba the black-breasted magpie was grinding quantities of doonbur, or grass seed, on his dayoorl. As he ground the seed he pushed it off the dayoorl into a bark wirree. He had a fire alongside him ready to cook the grass-seed cakes he was going to make.

When he had made a good number of his cakes, he would begin to sing as follows:

"Moograbalingo, go-oh, go-oh,
Moograbalingo, go-oh, go-oh,"

which was a call to such as heard it to come for food.

Any Daens, or blackfellows, hearing this cry would come, and after eating all they could, would lie down to sleep.

When Moogra-ba was sure that they were all asleep, he would steal away to his humpy, seize his birra-ga, or man-killing stick, come stealthily and kill the sleepers. He would then cook his victims and eat them, for he was a bunna, or cannibal.

Ooya, the quarrian parrot, and Gidgerigar, the small yellow-green parrot, were great wirinuns. Hearing of Moogra-ba's slaughters they determined to punish him.

These two told their tribes what they had discovered. Their tribes screamed at them, saying, "You are wirinuns. Kill him! Kill him! Burn him! Burn him!"

Before they set out to do so, Gidgerigar painted himself all yellow, put on his waistband and fastened to it a waywa, or fringe of kangaroo-rat skin, at each side, also at back and front. He put a white-painted band, called nulu-gail, around his hair, and around his forehead a garbai, or band, made of twisted opossum string. Ooya tied his hair into a walla-boondi, or topknot, painted his cheeks with red, gave a touch of red to his breasts, and put on his waywa, hair and forehead bands.

Each man carried a spear and a boondi. As they got near to Moogra-ba's camp they heard him sing out, "Come closer, come closer. I have nothing to eat."

But the two stood away. Moogra-ba, whose two wives were out hunting, sent over his two children to see if the strangers were fat. They ran back to their father, who said, "Are they fat?"

"Yes, they are fat," said the children.

Moogra-ba then took out some durri, or seed cakes, from the fire, and he and his children carried some over to the strangers, to whom they gave three cakes each.

Ooya and Giderigar said, "Were you calling out that we might come for you to give us these?"

"Yes," said Moogra-ba, "eat them. They are good."

They took the cakes and each ate two, keeping the third. When they had finished, Moogra-ba said, "Now that you have eaten you had better have a sleep. You will have headaches if you do not sleep after having eaten. Lie down. Lie down. One here and one there."

He pointed first on his right, then on his left.

They lay down, each taking care to have, on either side, a spear and a boondi.

Moogra-ba, to divert suspicion, lay down too, and soon they heard him snoring loudly. They put their waywas over their faces as if they too slept, but between the strands they watched Moogra-ba.

Gidgerigar just touched Ooya on the foot with his toe, as much as to say, "Do you hear him?" as Moogra-ba gave snore after snore.

Moogra-ba did not see this, and thought his guests were both asleep. After a while he raised himself on his hands and knees and looked well at them to see if they were really asleep.

They saw that he was watching them, and first one and then the other began to snore.

As louder and louder grew their snores Moogra-ba was at length assured that they were asleep. He then got up and ran over to his dardur, or bark humpy, to get his birra-ga.

Gidgerigar touched Ooya's foot again, and said softly, "Are you awake?"

"It's all right, I see him," replied Ooya.

They looked toward the dardur and saw Moogra-ba running back with his stick. As soon as he was well within spear range they both jumped up, seized their spears and called out, "That's what you do, old man, is it? This is how you trap the Daens, is it? Feed them first, and then kill them! We know all about you, and now your turn has come."

They then threw their spears at him. One struck through his side, one through his chest. Down he fell, and as he lay they ran up and hit him with their boondis on his skull and across his face. When they saw that he was quite dead they went back and killed his two boys. They dragged the bodies to where the father lay, and laid them on top of his.

Ooya and Gidgerigar then consulted whether they should wait for the two wives or go back. Ooya said, "Let us wait for the wives and kill them, too, while we are at it."

So it was decided. And when they saw the wives coming they hid themselves in the dardur. The women came along unsuspectingly. As they stopped to slip the handles of their goolays, or net bags, from under their arms and over their shoulders, so as to place them, and the yams and fruit they were full of, on the ground, out jumped the two men. Each man, seizing a woman, hit her on the back of her neck. And so both wives were killed, too.

Their bodies were then dragged to put on top of the others. Gidgerigar and Ooya then carried wood and piled it over all, set it on fire, and burned the lot.

They then gathered up all the wood they could find and heaped it over the burned bodies like a grave top.

But after they had gone, out flew a bird, calling:

> "Moogra-ba, go-oh, go-oh,
> Moogra-ba, go-oh, go-oh."

This was the cannibal Moogra-ba in a new form, a bird, black from the coals and white from the ashes he had had to struggle through to escape from under the heap of timber.

When Gidgerigar and Ooya reached their camp, the tribe called out, "How did you get on?"

"We killed the lot. One man, two boys, and two women."

The listeners gave a whirring sound of gladness with their lips and called out, "Well done! Well done!"

Ooya and Gidgerigar were themselves both turned into

birds afterward. Ooya's parrot tribe have always a topknot, and a red patch on each side of their beaks and on each breast, just as he had painted himself to kill Moogra-ba. And the traces of yellow are to be seen in the green of all Gidgerigar parrots' plumage, because of how the first Gidgerigar was painted that day. But in bird form neither answers the call they hear often in the bush, as they once did as men:

> "Moogra-ba, go-oh, go-oh,
> Moogra-ba, go-oh, go-oh."

Wayamba the Turtle

O O L A the lizard was out getting yams on a mirria flat. She had three of her children with her. Suddenly she thought she heard someone moving behind the big mirria bushes. She listened. All of a sudden out jumped Wayamba from behind a bush and seized Oola, telling her not to make a noise and he would not hurt her, but that he meant to take her off to his camp to be his wife. He would take her three children, too, and look after them.

Resistance was useless, for Oola had only her yam stick, while Wayamba had his spears and boondis. Wayamba took the woman and her children to his camp.

His tribe, when they saw him bring home a woman of the Oola tribe, asked him if her tribe had given her to him. He said, "No, I have stolen her."

"Well," they said, "her tribe will soon be after her. You must protect yourself, we shall not fight for you. You had no right to steal her without telling us. We had a young woman of our own tribe for you, yet you go and steal an Oola and bring her to the camp of the Wayambas. On your own head be the consequences."

WAYAMBA THE TURTLE

By this time you should be able to understand this sort of picture. However, don't mistake the thing at the top for anything other than a shield.

In a short time the Oolas were seen coming across the plain which faced the camp of the Wayambas. And they came not in friendship or to parley, for no women were with them. They carried no boughs of peace in their hands, but were painted as for war, and were armed with fighting weapons.

When all the Wayambas saw the approach of the Oolas, their wise man said, "Now, Wayamba, you had better go out on the plain and do your own fighting. We shall not help you."

Wayamba chose the two biggest boreens, or shields, that he had. One he slung on him, covering the front of his body, and one the back. Then, seizing his weapons, he strode out to meet his enemies.

When he was well out onto the plain, though still some distance from the Oolas, he called out, "Come on."

The answer was a shower of spears and boomerangs. As they came whizzing through the air Wayamba drew his arms inside the boreens, ducked his head down between them and so escaped.

As the weapons fell harmless to the ground, glancing off his boreen, out again he stretched his arms and held up again his head, shouting, "Come on, try again, I'm ready."

The answer was another shower of weapons, which he met in the same way. At last the Oolas closed in around him, forcing him to retreat toward the creek.

Shower after shower of weapons they slung at him, and were getting at such close quarters that his only chance was to dive into the creek. He turned toward the creek, tore the front boreen off him, flung down his weapons and plunged in.

The Oolas waited, spears poised in hand, ready to aim

the moment his head appeared above water, but they waited in vain.

Wayamba the blackfellow they never saw again. But in the water hole wherein he had dived they saw a strange creature, which bore on its back a fixed plate like a boreen. When they went to try and catch the creature it drew in its head and limbs. So they said, "It is Wayamba."

And this was the beginning of Wayamba, or turtle, in the creeks.

Wayamba the Turtle and Woggoon the Turkey

WAYAMBA the turtle was the wife of Goo-goor-gaga the laughing jackass. They had a quarrel when the time came for Wayamba to lay her eggs. She was going, as her tribe did, to the sand beside the creek, there to make a hole and deposit them. But Goo-goor-gaga said that was a mad thing to do, for a flood might come and wash them away. She should lay the eggs in a hollow tree.

Wayamba said, "How shall I get into a hollow tree? And even if I did get there, how should I get sand up to cover the eggs? And how would Yhi the sun shine on the sand to heat it and hatch them out?"

"How was I born, and my mother before me?" asked Goo-goor-gaga, answering her question with another, and going on, "My wife can surely do as our mothers did?"

"I am a Wayamba, and it is only right for me to do as the Wayambas do. Does a child not always take its name from its mother? My children will be Wayambas even as I am. I shall go to my own tribe."

Straight went Wayamba to the creek where her tribe lived. Into the water she went after them. Goo-goor-gaga followed her to the edge. Then he turned back and sent his messenger Wonga the pigeon, and Du-mer the brown pigeon, the wife of Wonga, after Wayamba.

Wonga sent Du-mer on to tell Wayamba to come back.

But Wayamba said, "No, I will not go back. Let him come himself if he wants me."

Wonga and Du-mer went back and told this to Goo-goor-gaga, who went as his wife had asked for him. But on the bank of the creek he saw the mother of Wayamba, so he turned back, for the law of the tribes did not let him speak to his mother-in-law. He sent Wonga to consult her.

"Tell him," said Wayamba the mother, "my daughter will not go back. He would have her break the laws of her tribe. She shall not leave her people."

Wonga went back to tell Goo-goor-gaga. Just as he was beginning to do so, out from the grass behind him crept Ooyu-bu-lui the black snake, an old lover of Wayamba's. Enraged at this messenger's wish to bring his old love back to the husband she had left, Ooyu-bu-lui meant to kill him. He was in the act of making a spring at Wonga to throttle him, when Goo-goor-gaga saw him.

Goo-goor-gaga made one dart and was on the back of Ooyu-bu-lui. Clutching hold of him, he flew high in the air, up, up, as far as his flight let him go, then he loosened his hold on Ooyu-bu-lui and let him drop swiftly, thud to the earth, his back broken. Down after him flew Goo-goor-gaga. There in his camp he saw his enemy lying dead.

"Twice have you tried to injure me, and twice have you failed," he said. "Once when you wanted to marry Wayamba, who was promised to me, and now when you wanted to kill my faithful messenger, sneaking as you did like a coward behind him. But instead of him, you yourself lie dead, powerless forever to harm me. So shall I always kill your treacherous tribe, against whom my people

shall have a dullay-mullay-lunna, or vengeful hatred, forever. Ah! But it is good to see you my enemy lying there."

And Goo-goor-gaga laughed long and loud peals of
laughter, until the whole creekside echoed with his startling
"Goo-goor-gaga. Goo-goor-gaga."

Startling indeed was the sound to Wayamba, for her
husband had always looked too solemn to laugh, except
when he had to herald the sunrise.

She hurried out of the water, and went away along
the opposite bank as fast as she could. She thought, as
peal after peal of his strange loud laughter reached her,
that her husband had gone mad, and that if he caught
her he would kill her. So near the laughter sounded that
she fancied he was pursuing her. She did not dare to look
around, but sped swiftly on.

But instead of following her, Goo-goor-gaga was eating
his enemy, and vowing again that so long as his tribe lived,
so long should they wage war against the tribe of Ooyu-
bu-lui, killing and eating them.

While this feast off her old lover was going on, Wayamba was putting an immense distance between herself
and her old camp. At length she was too tired to go
farther. She rested on a nice sandy place beside the creek.
There she decided to camp. She made a hole and laid her
eggs in it in due course. When the last was laid, and she
was carefully covering them up ready for the hatching, she
heard a sound on the bank above her. Looking up, she
saw there a dark-feathered bird, with a red head and neck,
peering down at her. On seeing her look up, the bird said,
"Why do you cover your eggs up?"

"That the sand and sun may hatch them."

"But won't you sit on them yourself?"

"No, indeed! Why should I do that? They will be warm
where they are, and come out even as I came out, in the

right time. If I sat on them I might break them. And who would get me food? I should die and they too."

The red-headed bird, which was Woggoon the brush turkey, went back to where her mate was feeding and told him what she had seen. She said she would like to try that plan; it seemed much easier than having to sit on the eggs week after week.

Her mate told her not to be in a hurry to change her ways; each tribe had its own custom. The Wayamba might only be fooling her. They would wait and see if the eggs came out all right. But even so he would not have his wife make a nest near the creek where a sudden rise of water might wash it away. They must stick to their scrub.

At length time proved that what Wayamba had said was true. The little Wayambas all came out, and were strong and well.

Then the Woggoons decided they would try and hatch their eggs without sitting on them. They could not dig a hole to lay them in, but they scratched up a heap of mixed rubbish, earth, sand, leaves and sticks. Then the mother Woggoon laid an egg every second day until fifteen were in the mound, all apart from each other, with the thin end downward. Over the eggs they put more decayed leaves and rubbish and, outside all, a heaped-up covering of more leaves and twigs. When all this was done the parents waited anxiously for the result.

As time went on the mother bird grew restless. What if she had killed all her young just to save herself? She fussed around the big mound which stood some feet high. She put her head in to feel if it were warm, then drew it out quickly, delighted to find the nest was absolutely hot. Then she began to fear it would be too hot. Full of anxiety she scratched away the earth and leaves, thinking the covering was too much. She stopped suddenly and listened.

Was that a baby-bird note? She listened again. It was. She called to her mate. He came, and when she told him what she had heard, he scratched away until to their joy out came the finest chicks they had ever seen, quite independent and strong, with feet and wings more advanced than any seen on their chicks before.

Proud of the success of her plan, and anxious to spread the good news, the mother Woggoon ran away from her family to tell all her tribe.

The next season the other Woggoons added to the size of the mound, and many of the mothers laid their eggs in one nest, until at last the whole tribe adopted the same plan, thus earning for themselves the name of Mound Builders.

Goola-willeels the Topknot Pigeons

Y O U N G Goola-willeel used to go out hunting every day. His mother and sisters always expected that he would bring home kangaroo and emu for them. But each day he came home without any meat at all. They asked him what he did in the bush, as he evidently did not hunt. He said that he did hunt.

"Then why," said they, "do you bring us nothing home?"

"I cannot catch and kill what I follow," he said. "You hear me cry out when I find kangaroo or emu, is it not so?"

"Yes. Each day we hear you call when you find something, and each day we get ready the fire, expecting you to bring home what you have killed, but you bring nothing."

"Tomorrow," he said, "you shall not be disappointed. I shall bring you a kangaroo."

Every day, instead of hunting, Goola-willeel had been gathering wattle gum, and with this he had been modeling a kangaroo—a perfect model of one, complete with tail,

219

ears and all. So the next day he came toward the camp carrying this kangaroo made of gum. Seeing him coming, and also seeing that he was carrying the promised kangaroo, his mother and sisters said, "Ah, Goola-willeel spoke truly. He has kept his word, and now brings us a kangaroo. Pile up the fire. Tonight we shall eat meat."

About a hundred yards away from the camp Boola-willeel put down his model, and came on without it. His mother called out, "Where is the kangaroo you brought home?"

"Oh, over there." And he pointed toward where he had left it.

The sisters ran to get it, but came back saying, "Where is it? We cannot see it."

"Over there," he said, pointing again.

"But there is only a great figure of gum there."

"Well, did I say it was anything else? Did I not say it was gum?"

"No, you did not. You said it was a kangaroo."

"And so it is a kangaroo. A beautiful kangaroo that I made all by myself." And he smiled quite proudly to think what a fine kangaroo he had made.

But his mother and sisters did not smile. They seized him, and gave him a good beating for deceiving them. They told him he should never go out alone again, for he only played instead of hunting, though he knew they starved for meat. They would always in the future go with him.

And so forevermore the Goola-willeels, the topknot pigeons, went in flocks, never singly, in search of food.

Gwai-nee-bu the Redbreast

G W A I - N E E - B U the redbreast and Goo-mai the water rat were down at the creek one day, getting mussels for food, when to their astonishment a kangaroo hopped right into the water beside them.

Well they knew that he must be escaping from hunters, who were probably pressing him close. So Gwai-nee-bu quickly seized her yam stick and knocked the kangaroo on the head. He was caught fast in the weeds in the creek, so could not escape.

When the two old women had killed the kangaroo, they hid its body under the weeds in the creek, fearing to take it out and cook it straightway, lest the hunters should come up and claim it. The little son of Gwai-nee-bu watched them from the bank.

After having hidden the kangaroo, the women picked up their mussels and started for their camp, when up came the hunters, Ooya and Gidgerigar, who had tracked the kangaroo right to the creek.

Seeing the women they said, "Did you see a kangaroo?"
The women answered, "No. We saw no kangaroo."

GWAI-NEE-BU THE REDBREAST

This one is quite easy to work out if you just twist it around slowly.
The dots and lines and black patches are hail and clouds from the
terrible storm that the women conjured up to get even with the
two men who wouldn't gve them any of the kangaroo.

"That is strange, for we have tracked it right up to here."

"We have seen no kangaroo. See, we have been digging out mussels for food. Come to our camp, and we will give you some when they are cooked."

The young men, puzzled, followed the women to their camp, and when the mussels were cooked the hunters joined the old women at their dinner.

The little boy would not eat the mussels. He kept crying to his mother, "Gwai-nee-bu. Gwai-nee-bu. I want kangaroo. I want kangaroo. Gwai-nee-bu. Gwai-nee-bu."

"There," said Ooya. "Your little boy has seen the kangaroo, and wants some. It must be here somewhere."

"Oh, no. He cries for anything he thinks of—some days for kangaroo. He is only a little boy, and does not know what he wants," said old Gwai-nee-bu.

But still the child kept saying, "Gwai-nee-bu. Gwai-nee-bu. I want kangaroo. I want kangaroo."

Goomai was so angry with little Gwai-nee-bu for keeping on asking for kangaroo, and thereby making the young men suspicious, that she hit him hard on the mouth to keep him quiet, so that the blood came and trickled down his breast, staining it red. When she saw this, old Gwai-nee-bu grew angry in her turn, and hit old Goomai, who returned the blow. And so a fight began, more words than blows. The noise was great, the women fighting, little Gwai-nee-bu crying—not quite knowing whether he was crying because Goomai had hit him, because his mother was fighting or because he still wanted kangaroo.

Ooya said to Gidgerigar, "They have the kangaroo somewhere hidden; let us slip away now in the confusion. We will only hide, then come back in a little while and surprise them."

They went quietly away, and as soon as the two women

noticed they had gone, they ceased fighting and determined to cook the kangaroo. They watched the two young men out of sight, and waited some time so as to be sure that they were safe. Then down they hurried to get the kangaroo. They dragged it out, and were just making a big fire on which to cook it, when up came Ooya and Gidgerigar, saying:

"Ah! We thought so. You had our kangaroo all the time. Little Gwai-nee-bu was right."

"But we killed it," said the women.

"But we hunted it here," said the men, and so saying caught hold of the kangaroo and dragged it away to some distance, where they made a fire and cooked it.

Goomai, Gwai-nee-bu and her little boy went over to Ooya and Gidgerigar, and begged for some of the meat, but the young men would give them none, though little Gwai-nee-bu cried piteously for some. But no, they said they would rather throw what they did not want to the hawks than give it to the women or child.

At last, seeing that there was no hope of their getting any, the women went away. They built a big dardur, or bark humpy, shutting themselves and the little boy up in it. Then they began singing a song which was to invoke a storm to destroy their enemies, for so now they considered Ooya and Gidgerigar. For some time they chanted:

> "Moogaray, Moogaray, May, May
> Eehu, Eehu, Doon-gara."

> "Hailstones, hailstones, wind, wind
> Rain, rain, lightning."

They began very slowly and softly, gradually getting quicker and louder, until at length they almost shrieked it out.

While they were chanting, little Gwai-nee-bu kept crying, and would not be comforted. Soon came a few big drops of rain, then a big wind, and as that lulled, more rain. Then came thunder and lightning, the air grew bitterly cold, and there came a pitiless hailstorm. Hailstones bigger than a duck's egg fell, cutting the leaves from the trees and bruising their bark. Gidgerigar and Ooÿa came running over to the dardur and begged the women to let them in.

"No," shrieked Gwai-nee-bu above the storm, "there was no kangaroo meat for us; there is no dardur shelter for you. Ask shelter of the hawks whom you fed."

The men begged to be let in, said they would hunt again and get kangaroo for the women, not one but many.

"No," again shrieked the women. "You would not even listen to the crying of a little child. It is better such as you should die."

And fiercer raged the storm and louder sang the women:

"Moogaray, Moogaray, May, May
Eehu, Eehu, Doon-gara."

So long and so fierce was the storm that the young men must have perished had they not been changed into birds. First they were changed into birds and afterward into stars in the sky, where they now are, Gidgerigar and Ooÿa, with the kangaroo between them, still bearing the names that they bore on the earth.

Narahdarn the Bat

N ARAHDARN the bat wanted honey.
He watched until he saw a Warra-nunna, or bee, alight.
He caught it, stuck a white feather between its hind legs,
let it go and followed it. He knew he could see the white
feather, and so follow the bee to its nest. He ordered his
two wives, of the Bilba, or sandhill rat tribe, to follow him
with wirrees to carry home the honey in. Night came on
and the Warra-nunna the bee had not reached his home.
Narahdarn caught him, imprisoned him under bark and
kept him safely there until next morning. When it was
light enough to see, Narahdarn let the bee go again, and
followed him to his nest, in a gun-yanni tree. Marking the
tree with his kumbu that he might know it again, he
returned to hurry on his wives who were some way behind.
He wanted them to come on, climb the tree and chop out
the honey.

When they reached the marked tree one of the women
climbed up. She called out to Narahdarn that the honey
was in a split in the tree. He called back to her to put her
hand in and get it out.

She put her arm in, but found she could not get it out again. Narahdarn climbed up to help her, but found when he reached her that the only way to free her was to cut off her arm. This he did before she had time to realize what he was going to do, and protest. So great was the shock to her that she died instantly.

Narahdarn carried down her lifeless body and commanded her sister, his other wife, to go up, chop out the arm and get the honey. She protested, declaring the bees would have taken the honey away by now.

"Not so," he said. "Go at once."

Every excuse she could think of, to save herself, she made. But her excuses were in vain, and Narahdarn only became furious with her for making them, and brandishing his boondi, drove her up the tree.

She managed to get her arm in beside her sister's, but there it stuck and she could not move it.

Narahdarn, who was watching her, saw what had happened and followed her up the tree. Finding he could not pull her arm out, in spite of her cries he chopped it off, as he had done her sister's. After one shriek, as he drove his kumbu through her arm, she was silent. He said, "Come down, and I will chop out the bees' nest."

But she did not answer him, and he saw that she, too, was dead.

Then he was frightened, and climbed quickly down the gun-yanni tree. Taking her body to the ground with him, he laid it beside her sister's and quickly hurried from the spot, taking no further thought of the honey.

As he neared his camp, two little sisters of his wives ran out to meet him, thinking their sisters would be with him, and that they would give them a taste of the honey. But to their surprise Narahdarn came alone, and as he drew near to them they saw his arms were covered with blood. And his face had a fierce look on it, which frightened them from even asking where their sisters were. They ran and told their mother that Narahdarn had returned alone, that he looked fierce and angry, also that his arms were covered with blood.

Out went the mother of the Bilbas, and she said, "Where are my daughters, Narahdarn? Forth went they this morning to bring home the honey you found. You come back alone. You bring no honey. Your look is fierce, as of one who fights, and your arms are covered with blood. Tell me, I say, where are my daughters?" (Here the mother-in-law broke a universal law, but this might be allowable on such an occasion.)

"Ask me not, Bilba. Ask Warra-nunna the bee, he may know. Narahdarn the bat knows nothing." And he wrapped himself in a silence that no questioning could pierce.

Leaving him there, before his camp, the mother of the Bilbas returned to her dardur and told her tribe that her daughters were gone, and Narahdarn, their husband, would tell her nothing of them. But she felt sure he knew their fate; and certain she was that he had some tale to tell, for his arms were covered with blood.

The wise man of her tribe listened to her. When she had finished and begun to wail for her daughters, whom she thought she would see no more, he said, "Mother of the Bilbas, your daughters shall be avenged if aught has happened to them at the hands of Narahdarn. Fresh are his tracks, and the young men of your tribe shall follow whence they have come, and finding what Narahdarn has done, swiftly shall they return. Then shall we hold a corroboree, and if your daughters fell at his hand, Narahdarn shall be punished."

The mother of the Bilbas said, "Well you have spoken, oh my relation. Now speed you the young men lest the rain fall or the dust blow and the tracks be lost."

Then forth went the fleetest-footed and the keenest-eyed of the young men of the tribe. Ere long, back they came to the camp with the news of the fate of the Bilbas.

That night was the corroboree held. The women sat around in a half-circle and chanted a monotonous chant, some of them keeping time by hitting two boomerangs together, and others by beating their rolled-up opossum rugs.

Big fires were lit on the edge of the scrub, throwing light on the dancers as they came dancing out from their camps, painted in all manner of designs, waywas, or belts, around their waists, tufts of feathers in their hair, and carrying in their hands painted wands. Heading the procession as the men filed out from the scrub into a cleared space in front of the women came Narahdarn. The light of the fires lit up the treetops, the dark belah trees showed out in fantastic shapes, and weird indeed was the scene as slowly the men danced around. Louder clicked the boomerangs, and louder grew the chanting of the women. Higher were the fires piled, until the flames shot their colored tongues around the trunks of the trees and high into the air.

One fire was bigger than all, and toward it the dancers edged Narahdarn.

Then the voice of the mother of the Bilbas shrieked in the chanting, high above that of the other women. As Narahdarn turned from the fire to dance back, he found a wall of men confronting him. These quickly seized him and hurled him into the madly leaping fire behind him, where he perished in the flames.

And so were the Bilbas avenged.

Wallu-barl the Bark Lizard

Every day, while the little camp children were playing and their parents were away hunting, a strange little boy used to come to the camp. He was only a little boy, about six or seven years old.

Every afternoon, after having played for some time with the other children, he would run away from them, go around the different dardurs and steal food out of them all, taking anything eatable he could find.

When the children saw him thus helping himself, they called out, "Don't touch our mothers' things!"

He did not heed them, but took what he wanted.

The children used to try and get back what he took. But when they came near to him he shot up suddenly taller and taller, far out of their reach. Having thus startled them into leaving him alone, he would escape to his own camp, the whereabouts of which no one knew.

At last the parents began to notice how much of their food was taken during their absence, and they said angrily to their children, "You eat all our food."

"No," they said, "we do not. It is a little boy who comes

while you are away. He comes along that track in the scrub."

The parents said, "Tomorrow we will wait for him, and see if you are telling the truth, for it would be a strange little boy who could steal all the food we miss every day."

Accordingly the next day the parents hid themselves in their humpies, instead of going out as usual.

The children played about, watching for the little boy. When they saw him coming one of them ran and told the parents.

Wallu-barl, after playing for a little while as usual, went to the first humpy and sat down, looking around for what he might take. After he had rested a few minutes he helped himself to some food, and was then moving on to the next humpy. But before he had time to go many steps, out the men and women rushed, yelling at him and brandishing boomerangs and boondis, which they soon threw at him. But to their surprise, even as their children had said, up he shot, growing taller and taller, while their weapons fell harmlessly around him. Seizing more, they threw another shower at him, aiming higher up, but he grew taller and taller, still unhurt. Then, dropping their remaining boomerangs and boondis, they caught hold of their spears and threw these with deadly force at him. As the spears pierced him, Wallu-barl fell dead.

As they saw him lying there, the Daens said, "He was our enemy, stealing our food. No need to bury him. We will only cover him with bark and change our camp."

This they did, and long afterward they saw creep from under the bark a little lizard. And they called it Wallu-barl, because they said it must be the spirit of the boy they had killed. And ever since then the little bark lizard has been called Wallu-barl.

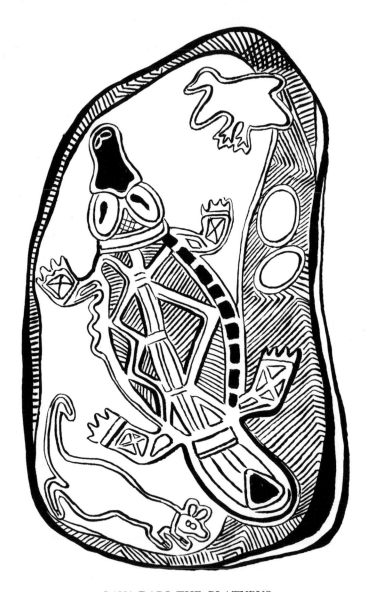

GAYA-DARI THE PLATYPUS

Poor little Gaya-dari needs a word or two of explanation since he is rather a hodgepodge. The truth is he had to be made up because Jubbul never told how to do a platypus (they didn't belong to his part of the country).

Gaya-dari the Platypus

A YOUNG duck used to swim away by herself in the creek. Her tribe told her that Mulloka the water devil would catch her some day if she were so venturesome. But she did not heed them.

One day after having swum down some distance she landed on a bank where she saw some young green grass. She was feeding about when suddenly Biggoon, an immense water rat, rushed out from a hidden place and seized her.

She struggled and struggled, but all in vain. "I live alone," he said. "I want a wife."

"Let me go," said the duck. "I am not for you. My tribe have a mate for me."

"You stay quietly with me, and I will not hurt you. I am lonely here. If you struggle more, or try to escape, I will knock you on the head, or spear you with this little spear I always carry."

"But my tribe will come and fight you, and perhaps kill me."

"Not they. They will think Mulloka has got you. But

even if they do come, let them. I am ready." And again he showed his spear.

The duck stayed. She was frightened to go while the rat watched her. She pretended that she liked her new life, and meant to stay always; while all the time she was thinking how she would escape. She knew her tribe came to look for her, for she heard them. But Biggoon kept her imprisoned in his hole in the side of the creek all day, only letting her out for a swim at night, when he knew her tribe would not come for fear of Mulloka.

She hid her feelings so well that at last Biggoon thought she really was content with him, and gradually he gave up watching her, taking his long day sleep as of old. Then came her chance.

One day, when Biggoon was sound asleep, she slunk out of the burrow, slid into the creek and swam away up it, as quickly as she could, toward her old camp.

Suddenly she heard a sound behind her. She thought it must be Biggoon, or perhaps the dreaded Mulloka, so, stiff as her wings were, she raised herself on them and flew the rest of the way, alighting at length very tired among her tribe.

They all gabbled around her at once, hardly giving her time to answer them. When they heard where she had been, the old mother ducks warned all the younger ones to swim only upstream in the future, for Biggoon would surely have vowed vengeance against them all now, and they must not risk meeting him.

How that little duck enjoyed her liberty and being with her tribe again! How she splashed as she pleased in the creek in the daytime and flew about at night if she wished! She felt as if she never wanted to sleep again.

It was not long before the laying season came. The ducks all chose their nesting places, some in hollow trees, and some in mirria bushes. When the nests were all nicely lined with down feathers, the ducks laid their eggs. Then they sat patiently on them until at last the little fluffy, downy ducks came out. Then in a little time the ducks in the trees took the ducklings on their backs and in their bills, and flew into the water with them, one at a time. Those in the mirria bushes waddled out with their young ones after them.

In due course the duck who had been imprisoned by Biggoon hatched out her young, too. Her friends came swimming around the mirria bush she was in, and said, "Come along. Bring out your young ones, too. Teach them to love the water as we do."

Out she came, only two children after her. And what were they? Such a quacking gabble her friends set up, shrieking, "What are those?"

"My children," she said proudly.

She would not show that she, too, was puzzled at her children's being quite different from those of her tribe. Instead of down feathers they had a soft fur. Instead of two feet they had four. Their bills were those of ducks, and their feet were webbed, and on the hind ones were just showing the points of a spear, like Biggoon always carried to be in readiness for his enemies.

"Take them away," cried the ducks, flapping their wings and making a great splash. "Take them away. They are more like Biggoon than us. Look at their hind feet; the tip of his spear is sticking from them already. Take them away, or we shall kill them before they grow big and kill us. They do not belong to our tribe. Take them away. They have no right here."

And such a row they made that the poor little mother duck went off with her two little despised children, of whom she had been so proud despite their peculiarities.

She did not know where to go. If she went down the creek Biggoon might catch her again, and make her live in the burrow, or kill her children because they had webbed feet, a duck's bill, and had been hatched out of eggs. He would say they did not belong to his tribe. No one would own them. There would never be anyone but herself to care for them. The sooner she took them right away the better.

So thinking, away upstream she went until she reached the mountains. There she could hide from all who knew her, and bring up her children. On and on she went, until the creek grew narrow and scrubby on its banks, so changed from the broad streams which used to flow placidly between large unbroken plains that she scarcely knew it. She lived there for a little while, then pined away and died, because even her children, as they grew, saw how different they were from her, and kept away by themselves, until she felt too lonely and miserable to live, too unhappy to find food. Thus pining she soon died, away on the mountains, far from her old noorumba, or hereditary hunting ground, which was hers by right of birth.

The children lived on and throve, laid eggs and hatched out more children just like themselves, until at last, pair by pair, they so increased that before long all the mountain creeks had some of them. And there they still live, the Gaya-dari, or platypus, quite a tribe apart—for when did ever a rat lay eggs? Or a duck have four feet?

Bubbur the Giant Brown-and-yellow Snake

B OODHA the lissome and soft-eyed was promised to Murree the swift-to-hunt-game, and the time was at hand when he could claim her. He was coming back from a Bora, back from the tests of courage, a warrior of his tribe, with the right to marry. Back to disappointment, and to despair.

First to meet him was Gubbi, the father of Boodha, in order to tell him the news of his promised wife.

She had been out hunting for honey, and she had come to the nest of a Bubbur, whence she had taken some eggs, bringing them back into the camp. Just as those who knew of the danger were scolding her for touching these, gliding into their midst had come the giant snake Bubbur. Past them all, straight to Boodha went Bubbur, coiled his form around hers and crushed the life from her. Then swiftly he went, as he had come, leaving Boodha the lissome and soft-eyed lifeless before them.

"Am I in time for the burial?" said Murree.

"Three times has Yhi slept since we buried her," said Gubbi.

"Then she is even now traveling toward Wi-bulloo, the heaven of women. I shall follow her. The dheal twigs are yet green on her path. I shall snatch her yet from Wi-bulloo."

"Think you," said Gubbi scornfully, "that she who was murdered will follow one who has not avenged her?"

Then Murree paused from slaying himself where he stood, and he said, "There is wisdom in your words, Gubbi. I shall first slay Bubbur, the snake demon."

Thus saying, Murree turned to the camp of his tribe.

The days passed, and Boodha was still unavenged. But Murree never forgot her. Nor did he cast one glance on the comeliest of maidens. His heart was with Boodha in Wi-bulloo. His mind was bent on revenge.

He went hunting with two of his tribe. At length he saw what he wished for ahead of him. A nest of the Bubburs was there. He did not run straight to attack it, as his mullayas, or mates, expected, but went back with them to the camp.

"Come," he said to his tribe, "come and let us gather the gum of mubbu."

He told them then why he spoke so, and seeing his reason was good, they followed him. Having gathered the mubbu, or beefwood, gum in plenty, they carried it back to their camp.

Next day they went with Murree, and at his bidding broke down the branches of trees some distance from the nest of the Bubburs. With these branches they made platforms on the boughs of some trees that he showed them. They went onto these platforms, and the noise they made was great. Upon hearing it, out came the snakes, the giant Bubburs. Murree and the Daens had been careful that no shadow of theirs should fall on the ground. They knew well that should a Bubbur bite even their shadows, it would kill them.

As the Bubburs came nearer and nearer, the Daens made ready pieces of mubbu gum, about the size of a pigeon's egg, to throw at their mouths. Snap went the jaws of the Bubburs at them. Another pellet of gum was thrown. Snap! and the jaws, the jaws of death, were closed, held fast by the gum between them!

The murderous Bubburs were mastered. Murree the avenger had conquered!

Seeing the scheme had worked as they wished, the Daens returned to their camp. There they waited patiently, returning in due time to the scene of their gum throwing. They were laden with wood, for they expected to find their enemies dead, and the flesh of Bubburs was good. Great was the joy of Murree when he saw the gum had stuck their jaws fast, and that the Bubburs were all dead. His hand was swift to raise his kumbu and sever their heads from their bodies. Swift, too, were the Daens in lighting fires for cooking the Bubburs.

And Bubburs have been scarce in the land since Boodha the lissome and soft-eyed was avenged by the cunning of Murree the swift-to-hunt-game.

Even so, their name carries terror yet to its hearer. Their size has grown with the time, and fear has stretched their measurements, until even the strongest and wariest feel a tremor when the name of the brown-and-yellow Bubbur is mentioned.

Eerin the Small Gray Owl

ERIN the Daen was a very light sleeper. When at night an enemy tried to steal into the camp, to spear someone of the tribe or crack a skull with his boondi, there was no chance of his being able to do so if Eerin was there. For no sooner did the enemy get within spearshot of the camp than Eerin would cry out, "Mil! Mil! Mil!" which was, "Eye! Eye! Eye!" meaning his tribe were to look out, there was danger threatening.

And when at length Eerin died, the Daens all grieved much, saying that now indeed their enemies would sneak upon them, and they be unwarned, for none could hear as did Eerin the light sleeper.

They placed the body of Eerin in a bark coffin, which they painted all over with red ocher. Before the ocher dried the oldest wirinun ran his thumbnail from one end to the other, then across the coffin, leaving thus divisions in the ocher, forming a cross. This done they corroboreed round the coffin, singing one of the death chants. Toward evening they lifted up the coffin and carried it to the grave they had dug. The mourners were all painted, and had leaves and feathers in their hair, twigs from the sacred dheal tree around their wrists, knees, ankles and waists, also through the holes in the cartilage of their noses. They carried bunches of dheal twigs, too, in their hands.

When they reached the grave they laid some logs in the bottom, which they thickly covered with dheal twigs, on the top of which they put the coffin. A wail went up from all assembled, the mournful death wail of the tribe, rising and falling in waves.

Then an old wirinun stood up and spoke, telling them that as Eerin was now, so some day they all would be. Thus it behooved them to keep well the laws of Baiame, lest when their spirits reached Bullima they would not be allowed to stay or to wander at will, but would be sent to the Eleänba Wunda, in the place of the wicked.

After this speech, more twigs were thrown on the coffin, then the things belonging to the dead were placed in the grave—rugs, weapons and food—which would be wanted on the journey to the sacred mountain, Oobi Oobi.

While this was being done the oldest male relative stood in the grave to guard the body from the Wunda, or evil spirits, until the earth covered it. He stood there while a chant somewhat as follows was sung:

"We shall follow the bee to its nest in the coolabah;
We shall follow it to its nest in the bibbil tree.
Honey too shall we find in the goori tree,
But Eerin the light sleeper will follow with us no
    longer."

Then the mourners wailed until the wirinuns chanted again:

"Many were the days when we took our nets to the river;
Many and big were the codfish we caught in them,

But Eerin the light sleeper will go no more to the river;
No more will he rub himself with the oil of codfish,
Eerin will never eat again of the codfish."

Then, as the wirinuns paused, the wailing was loud
again until they began once more the dirge:

"We shall spear Bohra on the morillas,
And Dinewan shall fall when we throw,
But Eerin will hunt with us no longer,
Never again will Eerin eat of our hunting.
Hunt shall we often, and oft shall we find;
But the widow of Eerin will kindle
    no fires for his coming."

Loud again was the wailing, then on went the voice of
the wirinuns:

"Never again shall the voice of the light sleeper
Cry, 'Mil, Mil, Mil,' as an enemy nears us.
Cracked will our skulls be and speared our bodies.
Eerin can warn us no more with his cry,
Only his spirit can come to us ever, an offering let
    us now pour to it."

Then with loud wailing, seizing stone knives and kumbus, the mourners cut themselves, letting their blood drop
into the grave. Never before was there such a blood offering.
Then the earth was thrown quickly into the grave, while
some of the mourners corroboreed round it, crooning a
dirge.

When the earth was filled in, all stood in a dense
smoke that the wirinuns had made of boodha twigs, which
was to keep them free from the unseen spirits known to be
hovering round.

When the grave was filled in, back to their new camp
went the women, for the old one was now gunmarl, a

place of death, with a marked tree showing it was taboo, not to be visited.

No children, or women with children who could not walk, were allowed to go to the funeral.

After the women left, all the men stood around the grave, the oldest wirinun at the head, which faced the east. The men bowed their heads as if at a first Bora, the wirinun lifted his, and looking toward where Bullima was supposed to be, said, "Baiame, let in the spirit of Eerin to Bullima. Save him, we ask you, from the Eleänba Wunda, in the place of the wicked. Let him into Bullima, there to roam as he wills, for Eerin was great on earth and faithful ever to your laws. Hear, then, our cry, O Baiame, and let Eerin enter the land of beauty, of plenty, of rest. For Eerin was faithful on earth, faithful to the laws you left us."

Then, standing around the grave, all wailed the goonai, or death dirge.

Then the men covered the grave with boughs of dheal trees and swept a clear space all around it. By the tracks on that space in the morning they would know of what mäh, or totem, was he who had caused the death of Eerin. If on it was the track of an iguana, then had one of the Beewee, or iguana, clan done it; if the track of an emu, then was a Dinewan guilty.

The widow of Eerin had put mud over herself, daubing her head and face with white. She slept beside a smoldering smoke all night.

Three days afterward the Daens made a fire by the river. They chased the widow and her sisters down to it. The widow caught hold of a smoking bush from the fire, put it under her arm and jumped into the middle of the water. As the smoking bush was going out she drank a draught of the smoky water. Then she came out and stood in the smoke of the fire. When she was thoroughly enveloped in the smoke she called to those in the camp, and looking toward her husband's grave, she called again. Those in the camp called to her that his spirit had answered; she might speak now. She had been obliged to keep silence, except for death wails, since Eerin's death.

Back she went to the camp. A big smoke was made, and the whole camp smoked. Everytime a stranger came the widow made a smoke, until the time arrived when the nearest of her husband's kin could claim her for his own.

For some months after the death of Eerin, everytime a stranger came to the camp, early the next morning he would sing the goonai, or dirge; then each man would take part in turn, until all were singing. Then they all moved out of their camps and gradually closed round into a smaller circle, when they would cease singing, sit down, and rocking their bodies to and fro, they would cry and wail.

When the time of mourning was over, an enemy came again to attack them, but they were saved by hearing the old cry of "Mil! Mil! Mil!"

And so it often happened.

At last an enemy died and carried his hatred of them to another world, whence he returned as a spirit to attack them. But again they were saved by the warning cry of "Mil! Mil! Mil!"

This cry they discovered was made by a little gray owl with black rings around its eyes, which, having warned the camp, flew from it. The Wunda, or evil spirit, saw it and said, "Why do you warn them? Keep quiet next time I go to sneak upon them. See, I have my boondi. I will kill one of the tribe quickly, and you can join me in my feast of his flesh."

The bird promised silence, and the Wunda went again

into the camp. But just as he was going to raise his boondi to deal a fatal blow, "Mil! Mil! Mil!" was cried in the sleeper's ear.

The owl had followed the Wunda into the camp.

"Why did you do that?" the Wunda angrily asked.

"That I shall always do, even as when I was Eerin the man, for did not my tribe spill freely the blood offering? Shall I not then save them from the Wunda even as I did from their old enemies? By day I shall rest, and at night I shall roam, hovering round their camps to guard them, by my cry, when danger threatens them."

And so it has been ever since. The spirit of Eerin the light sleeper is in the little gray owl, which is called Eerin too, and ever warns its old tribe at night by crying, "Mil! Mil! Mil!"

Pronunciation

a as in *far* or *mat*. Example: *bargi*, a grandmother; *mullian*, eagle-hawk.

e as in *fed* or *ey* in *obey*. Example: *Dinewan*, an emu; *yunbeai*, an animal familiar.

i as in *fit*, in the middle of a word, though may be as *ee* in *see*, and at end as *y* in *happy*. Example: *dilli* (bag); *Riverina; wi*, clever.

o as in *toe*, or as in *on*. Example: *mulloka*, a water devil; *brolga*, a native companion.

u as in *fun*, or *oo* as in *moon*, more especially at the end of a word. Example: *wunda*, a spirit; *gruee* (groo-ee), a species of tree; *mubbu* (mub-boo), beefwood tree (first *u* short, second long).

ai as *i* in *wine*. Example: *Baiame* (Baia:me), accent on second *a*.

g beginning a word is always hard, as in *go*. Example: *gubba*, good.

gg and *gh* also hard. Example: *biggoon*, a water rat; *Gheeger Gheeger*, the cold west wind.

ng soft as in *singer*. Example: *binga-wingul*, needlebush.

ngg hard as in *finger*. Example: *mingga*, a spirit tree; *munggi*, a mussel.

dh as the *th* in *than*. Example: *dheal*, a sacred tree; *eer-dher*, a mirage.

y was always used as a consonant in a neighboring language, according to one authority; and, it seems, often here. Example: *bun-yal*, flies; *a* here long, as in *far*. As usual in our own language, a double consonant shortens the vowel.

Glossary

Spellings are as used in the text. Mrs. Langloh Parker's original spellings, also her alternatives, are given in round brackets. Often there was a difference between the spelling of words in her text and those in the vocabularies (taken from three books of legends and *The Euahlayi Tribe*). Meanings given as Mrs. Langloh Parker's, also taken from these four books.

Bahal: a tree
Bahloo: the moon (masculine)
Bahn: mistletoe
Baiame (Byamee): literal meaning, "Great One"; culture hero or god; creator
Baiamul (byahmul): black swan [The change in spelling follows that of the preceding word, since reference is made to "birds of Byamee."—H.D.-B.]
Bargi(e): mother's mother, i.e. grandmother
Barwon: river in New South Wales
Beela (also beeleer and beeler): black cockatoo
Beereeun: small prickly lizard
Beewee: iguana
Belah: a tree [Bull oak.—H.D.-B.]
Berai Berai: the boys; Orion's belt and sword
Biaga (beeargah): a hawk
Bibbi (bibbee): woodpecker
Bibbil: broad-leafed box tree; eucalyptus

Biboh: cry of the black swan

Biggoon: water rat

Bilba (also bilby, bilber): large rat, living in sandhills [Bandicoot.— H.D.-B.]

Billai (or billay): crimson-wing parrots

Billoo: eagle-footed men

Bindia (bindeah): a prickle

Binga-wingul (bingahwingul): needlebush (scrub)

Bingge-la (bingehlah): exclamation, or "you can have it"

Bingui(e): a coolamon, or wooden canoe-shaped vessel for water

Bira(h): a whitewood tree

Brra-ga: man-killing stick

Birra-li (birrahlee): baby

Birra-nulu (Birrahgnooloo): woman's name meaning "face like a tomahawk handle;" Baiame's first wife.

Birrarl: an exclamation

Birri gu gu (birree gougou): "sool 'em"

Birwain: bulrush

Bohra(h) (also bowrah): kangaroo

Booboo-tella (boobootella): emu tail feathers

Boodha (büdtha, budta, budtah): rosewood tree or polygonum shrub; a girl's name; salt [Note the *dh* is pronounced much as *th* in *the*.— H.D.-B.]

Boogira: a place name

Boogoo: a long club

Boogoo-doo-ga-da (boogoodoogahdah): the rain bird

Boolee: whirlwind

Booma-ooma-nowi (boomahoomahnowee): son of Baiame

Boondi (also boondee): club-headed weapon

Bootoolga(h): blue-gray crane

Bora (Borah, Boorah): sacred initiation rites and ceremonies

Boreen: wooden shield

Brewarrina: a place near Dirangibirra

Brolga (bralgah): native companion; crane; also Magellanic Clouds

Buba-larmay (bubahlarmay): game played by jumping into the water with a splash

Bubbera(h): boomerang that returns

Bubbur(r): giant yellow-and-brown snake

Buggoo: flying squirrel

Bukkandi (buckandee, also buckandeer): native cat

Bulga-nunnoo (bulgahnunnoo): bark-backed, i.e. insects under the bark of logs

Bulla(h) Bulla(h): butterflies

Bullai Bullai: green parrot

Bullima(h): sky camp; heaven

Bulli-medi-mundi (bullimedeemundi): southeast

Buln Buln: green parrot

Bulooral (boolooral): night owl

Bu-maya-mul (Boomayahmayahmul): wood lizard

Bumbel (bumble): native orange

Bunmilla(h): a fish

Bunna: cannibal

Bun-yal (bunnyyarl, bunnyal): flies

Bun-yun Bun-yun (bungun bungun): frog

Butterga(h): girl's name; species of flying squirrel

Coolabah: flooded box tree; eucalyptus

Coorigil (also Corrigel, Courigul): place name; sign of bees

Corroboree (corrobboree): aborigines' dance

Daen: a blackfellow [Euahlayi word used as one would use "an Australian."—H.D.-B.]

Dardur(r): bark humpy or shelter

Daya(h)-minya(h): small carpet snake

Dayoorl: flat stone for grinding grass seed

Deenyi: iron-bark tree

Deereeree: willie wagtail, a small bird

Degeenboya(h): soldier bird

Dhé: hereditary totem

Dheal: sacred tree of the Noonga(h)burra(h)s, used only for placing on the graves of the dead [Note: *dh* pronounced as our *th*.— H.D.-B.]

Dilli (dillee): dillibag; treasure bag

Dindi (dindee): pointed stick

Dinewan: emu

Dinjerra(h): the west

Dirangibirra(h): a place near Brewarrina

Doogoober(h): a place on the seacoast

Dooliba (dulibah): bald

Dooloomai: thunder

Doonbur(r): grass seed

Doon-gara (doongara, doongairah): lightning

Dooran Dooran (dourandouran, dourandowran): the north wind

Doori: a grunting dayoorl or grinding stone

Doowi (doowee): dream spirit

Dullay-mullay-lunna (dullaymullaylunnah): a feud or vendetta
[Literal meaning, vengeful hatred.—H.D.-B.]

Dulloora(h): small gray bird

Du-mer (dumerh, dummerh): brown pigeon

Dungel (dungle): a water hole

Dunger(h): a place

Durri(e): cake of grass-seed flour

Durroon: night heron

Eehu: rain (U e hu in song only)

Eer-dher (also eer-dheer): a mirage

Eer-moonän (earmoonan, ear-mounan): long sharp teeth; a monster

Eerin: a small gray owl

Eleänba(h) Wunda(h): two-toed spirit monsters of the underworld

Euahlayi: language of Narran River tribes; also spelled Youali,
Yualayi, etc.

Eurah: a drooping shrub

Galah (gilah): pink-breasted parrot

Ga-ra-ga (gahrahgah): crane

Garbai: a forehead band of string

Garbarli (garbarlee): shingle-back

Gaya-dari (gayardaree): platypus

Gayandi (also gayanday, gayandy): man's name for Bora spirit; a
bull-roarer; Bora devil. Gurraymi, gurraymy, woman's name for
the same

Gheeger Gheeger: the cold west wind

Ghinda-inda-mui (Ghindahindahmoee): son of Baiame

Gidgerigar (gidgereegah): a species of small parrot

Gidya: tree of acacia species, which gives forth a sickening smell in
damp weather, or when in bloom

Gilguy: water hole

Girra(h)ween: place of flowers

Goodoo: codfish

Googarh: iguana

Goo gool gai ya (googoolguyyah): "turn into trees"

Googoorewon: the place of trees (Goorewon, a tabooed woman)

Goo-goor-gaga (gougourgahgah, goug gour gahgah): laughing jackass; literal meaning, "take a stick"

Go-oh: come

Goola-gool (goolahgool, goolahyool): water-holding tree

Goola(h)-willeel: topknot pigeon

Goolay: netted string bag

Goolay-yali (goolayyahlee): pelican

Gooloo: magpie

Goomai: water rat

Goombeelga(h): bark canoe

Goomble-gubbon (goomblegubbon): turkey, or bustard of the plains

Goomilla(h): woman's string dress; young girl's dress, consisting of waist strings of opossum's sinews with strands of woven opossum's hair hanging about a foot square in front

Goonagulla(h): the sky

Goo(h)nai: death wail

Goonbean: sugar specks on the leaves of the bibbil tree

Goonur: kangaroo rat

Goori: a tree

Gooweera: poison stick or bone (used in pointing)

Gowa-gay (gowargay): emu in Milky Way

Gruee (grooee): handsome tree bearing plumlike fruit, tart and bitter but much liked by the aborigines

Gubba: good

Gubbera(h): clear magic stone; crystal

Gubbi (gubbee): a man's section name (one of four social sections of the tribe) [also spelled Kubbee, in *The Euahlayi Tribe*.—H.D.-B.]

Gudda(h): red lizard

Gulli (gullee): water

Gulli-maya (gulleemeah): water bags

Gundablui (Gundablouie): a place

Gundooi (also goondooi, gundooee): one emu living alone; a solitary emu

Gunmarl: taboo; a place where someone has died

Gunni (gunnai): yam sticks

Gunyah: bark shelter

Gun-ya-mu (gunyahmoo): southeast wind; also gunyahnoo

Gun-yanni (gunyanny): a tree

Gurburra(h): the north

Gurraymi (gurraymy): Bora spirit; *see* Gayandi

Gwai: red

Gwai-billa(h): the red star; Mars

Gwai-nee-bu (gwineeboo, guineeboo): robin redbreast

Gweebet (guiebet): a thorny creeper bearing masses of myrtlelike flowers, and edible fruit resembling passion fruit

Irra(h)-deeboo-la(rh): having toothless jaws

Kumbi (comebee, cumbee): bag made of kangaroo skins

Kumbooran: the east

Kumbu (comeboo, comebo): stone tomahawk or ax

Kunnan-beili (Cunnembeille, Cunnunbeille): girl's name meaning pigweed root; Baiame's second wife

Kurrajong: a tree; Noonga

Kurria (kurreah): crocodile

Kwa: a dance of crows

Madhi (Mahthi): dog [Note: *dh* as *th.*]

Mäh: totem; brand; hand

Mai-ra: paddymelon

May, Mayr: wind

Mayama (also with h, and maimah): stones

Maya-mayi (Meamei): the girls, the seven sisters; Pleiades

Mayra(h): the spring wind

Midjee: a tree, species of acacia

Midjeer: stick with barbed end

Mil: eye

Millia (millair, millear): kangaroo rat

Millin-dulu-nubba (Millindooloonubbah): widow's name; a bird

Mingga(h): spirit-haunted tree

Mirria (mirrieh): polygonum shrub

Moodai: opossum

Moogaray: hailstones

Moogra-ba (moograbah): black-breasted magpie

Mooregoo: mopoke, a dull-witted person

Mooroola(h): a weapon, a waddy, an aboriginal war club

Mooroomin (murroomin): bark of noonga(h) [kurrajong] tree

Mooroon: an emu spear (also moornin, moonoon)

Mooroonu-mil-da(h): having no eyes

Mooyi (Mouyi): white cockatoos with yellow crests; the north and
south points of the Southern Cross

Morilla(h) (also moorillah): stony or pebbly ridge

Mubboon: small tributary

Mubbu (mubbo, mubboo): beefwood tree

Muggil: stone knife

Mullaya (mullayerh): mate, in the sense of friend or companion

Mullee Mullee: dream spirit (of a wirinun)

Mullian (mullyan): eagle-hawk

Mullian-ga (mullyangah): chief of eagle-hawks; the Morning Star

Mulloka: water devil

Mulubinba: a place

Munde(h)-wudda(h) (mundehwaddah): northwest wind

Munggi (mungghee): mussel

Munggi-wurray-mul (mungghee wurraywurraymul): sea gull

Mungoon-gali (mungoongarlee): iguana

Murga(h) Muggai(gui): trap-door spider

Murra-wunda(h) (wondah): climbing rat

Murree: species of fish; the swift-to-hunt-game

Murrumbidgee: a river

Naia-lerh Nuddu-waighi: "I am a spirit opossum"

Narahdarn: bat

Narine: a place

Narran (Narrin): name of river

Na-wo (gnahwo): yes

Nerangledool: a place

Nindeegoolee: a place

Noondoo: a place

Noonga(h): kurrajong tree

Noonga(h)burra(h): tribe of blacks on the Narran River; belonging
to the Noonga(h) country

Noora(h)-gogo: orange-and-blue beetle

Noorumba(h): hereditary hunting ground

Nulla(h)-nulla(h): heavy-headed club

Nulu-gail (gnooloo-gail): white-painted headband

Nulu-yoon-du (Gnoolooyoundoo): name of a monster

Num-ba-di (numbardee): mother, mother's sister

Nunnoo (also nyunnoo): grass humpy or shelter

Nuru-buan (nurroobooan): south (also nurroolooan)
Nuru-nuru-bin (nooroonooroobin): south wind

Oobi Oobi: Baiame's sacred mountain dwelling place, in the other
  world
Ooboon: blue-tongued lizard
Oodoolay: a round rainmaking stone
Oola(h): red prickly lizard
Ooya (ouyah, ouyarh): quarrian parrot
Ooyan: curlew
Ooyu-bu-lui (ouyouboolooey): black snake

Piggi(e)-billa(h): anteater; porcupine; one of the Echnidna, a mar-
  supial

Tukki (tucki): fish, a species of bream

U e hu: rain (in song only)

Wa-ah: shells
Waddies: aboriginal war clubs
Wahgoo (also whagoo): a game like hide and seek
Wahl (also Youal, Euahl): no
Wahler (wahlerh): manna running down the stems of trees
Wahn: crow
Walla-boondi (wallahboondee): topknot
Walla-gudjail-wan (Wallahgudjailwan, Waddahgudjaelwon): female
  spirit in charge of spirit children awaiting incarnation
Wall-guroon-bu-an (Wallagooroonbooan): Baiame's messenger; a
  male spirit kind to children
Wallu-barl (walloobahl): bark lizard
Warooga (wahroogah): child
Warrambool: flood-water overflow on polygonum flats; the Milky
  Way
Warra-nunna (warranunnah, wurranunnah): bee
Wayamba (wayambah, wayambeh): turtle
Waywa(h): belts worn by men, consisting of a waistband of opos-
  sum's sinews, with bunches of strips of paddymelon skins hanging
  from them
Way Way: devil's bread, fungus
Weedah: the mockingbird; bowerbird

Wi: clever; a small fish

Wi-bulloo: fire; name of women in fireless country of legend

Widder Murtee: a place near Brewarrina

Wilgu-wilgu (willgoo-willgoo, wilgoo-wilgoo): painted stick with feathers on top

Wi-oombeen (weeombeen): small bird like robin redbreast

Wirinun (wirreenun): literal meaning, "clever-man"; medicine man; sorcerer; a fully initiated man; a learned person [See *wi*, above, given by Mrs. Langloh Parker as "clever," and compare use of wirree in the following words.—H.D.-B.]

Wirree: canoe-shaped bark vessel for water

Wirreebeeun: a young woman or adolescent girl

Wirreebilla: big water hole in Barwon River

Woggara(h): wooden battle ax

Woggi (wogghee): plains [Cf. "woggheeguy" (stories from the plains? Mrs. Langloh Parker calls them "fairy stories"), "woggigai".—H.D.-B.)

Woggoon: brush turkey; a mound builder

Womba(h): mad or deaf; Canopus

Wonga: pigeon

Wunda(h) (Wondah): spirits; ghosts; white people; white devils

Wurley: shelter

Wurra-wilberoo (wurrahwilberoo): whirlwind with devils in it; two dark patches in the Milky Way; also Magellanic Clouds

Wurrunna(h): man's name; a culture hero?

Wyah: an exclamation

Yaraän: white gum tree

Yaraänba: place of white gum tree

Yaraändoo: place of white gum tree; the Southern Cross

Yarraga (Yarrageh): the spring wind (also Mayra)

Yhi: the sun (feminine)

Yowi (yowee): spirit surviving death of body; also warning spirit of death; a soul equivalent

Yuaia (Youayah): frogs

Yualayi: the language spoken by the Noonga(h)burra(h) tribe [Now the accepted spelling of Euahlayi.—H.D.-B.]

Yukkay (Yuckay): an exclamation, "oh dear!"

Yulu-mara (euloomarah): grubs

Yulu-wirree (euloowirree): rainbow

Yunbeai: individual totem; familiar spirit